# Questions and Answers

# MATHEMATICS

KEY STAGE 4

# to A*

**Mark Patmore**  Principal Examiner

**Brian Seager**  Chief Examiner

SERIES EDITOR: BOB McDUELL

EDUCATIONAL

# Contents

## HOW TO USE THIS BOOK

The purpose of the *Questions and Answers* series is to help you achieve the grades you want in your GCSEs. This book is designed to help all students aiming for an A or A* grade and also provides a good basis for revision for the Standard Grade of the Scottish Certificate of Education, Credit Level. The companion title to this book, *GCSE Questions and Answers Mathematics*, also contains questions which are focused on the Higher tier (A*–C) papers, and will therefore provide invaluable general practice for all students aiming for A and A*.

This book is based on the idea that an experienced Examiner can give, through exam questions, sample answers and advice, the help you need to secure success. Many revision aids concentrate on providing the facts which might have to be remembered in an exam. This book focuses on giving you invaluable practice at doing exam questions, so that you can learn to improve your exam technique.

The *Questions and Answers* series is designed to provide:

● Easy to use **Revision Summaries** which identify the important facts. These are to remind you, in summary form, of the topics you will need to have revised in order to answer exam questions. (Answers to the illustrative examples are also provided.)

● Advice on the different types of question in each subject and how to answer them well to obtain the highest marks.

● Many examples of **exam questions**, with spaces for you to fill in your answers, just as in an exam. It is best if you try the questions first before going to the answers and the advice which accompanies them. The questions are either official Exam Board questions or have been specially written by experienced Examiners who write questions for the Exam Boards.

● **Sample answers** to all of the questions.

● **Examiner's tips.** By using the experience of Examiners we are able to give advice on how your answers can be improved, and how common mistakes can be avoided.

## THE IMPORTANCE OF USING QUESTIONS FOR REVISION

Past exam questions play an important part in revising for examinations. However, it is important not to start practising questions too early. Nothing can be more disheartening than trying to do a question that you do not understand because you have not mastered the concepts. Therefore it is important to have studied a topic thoroughly before attempting questions on it.

It is unlikely that any question you try will appear in exactly the same form on the papers you are going to take. However the number of totally original questions that can be set on any part of the syllabus is limited and so similar ideas occur over and over again. It certainly will help you if the question you are trying to answer in an exam is familiar and you are used to the type of language used. Your confidence will be boosted, and confidence is important for exam success.

Practising exam questions will also highlight gaps in your knowledge and understanding that you can go back and revise more thoroughly.

Finally, having access to answers, as you do in this book, will enable you to see clearly what is required by the Examiner, how best to answer each question and the amount of detail required.

## MAXIMISING YOUR MARKS IN MATHEMATICS

One of the keys to exam success is to know how marks are gained or lost and the Examiner's tips given with the solutions in this book give hints on how you can maximise your marks on particular questions. However, you should also take careful note of these general points:

- Check the requirements of your exam board and follow the instructions (or 'rubric') carefully. Many mathematics papers start with short, straightforward questions. You should work through them in order, so that you build up your confidence. Do not overlook any parts of a question – double-check that you have seen everything, including any questions on the back page! Take time to read through all the questions carefully, and then start with the question you think you can do best.

- Get into the habit of setting out your work neatly and logically. If you are untidy and disorganised you could penalise yourself by misreading your own figures or lose marks because your method is not obvious. Always show all necessary working so that you can obtain marks for a correct method even if your final answer is wrong. Remember that a good clear sketch can help you to see important details.

- When the question asks for a particular result to be established, remember that to obtain the method marks you must show sufficient working to convince the Examiner that your argument is valid.

- Do not be sloppy with algebraic notation or manipulation, especially involving brackets and negatives. Do rough estimates of calculations to make sure that they are reasonable, state units if applicable and give answers to the required degree of accuracy; do not approximate too early in your working.

- Make sure that you are familiar with the formulae at the front of the exam paper and learn any useful formulae that are not included.

- When about 15 minutes remain, check whether you are running short of time. If so, try to score as many marks as possible in the short time that remains, concentrating on the easier parts of any questions not yet tackled.

- The following glossary may help you in answering questions:
  **Write down, state** – no explanation needed for an answer.
  **Calculate, find, show, solve** – include enough working to make your method clear.
  **Deduce, hence** – make use of the given statement to establish the required result.
  **Sketch** – show the general shape of a graph, its relationship with the axes and points of special significance.
  **Draw** – plot accurately, using graph paper and selecting a suitable scale; this is usually preparation for reading information from the graph.
  **Find the <u>exact</u> value** – leave in fractions, roots or $\pi$ and note that using a calculator is likely to introduce decimal approximations, resulting in loss of marks.

## DIFFERENT TYPES OF EXAM QUESTION

There are different types of question which appear on exam papers. Questions on mathematics papers are of three types:

### 'Pure' mathematics questions

These are usually short and are focused on one particular skill or part of the syllabus.

> Example 1:  Solve the equation $x^2 - 3x - 40 = 0$.

> Answer _____(2)

### Structured questions

These are the most common type of question in GCSE Mathematics papers and thus most of the questions in this book are structured questions. These questions usually have a context – that is they are about the application of mathematics to a real (or nearly real!) situation.

A structure is built into the question and, hence, into your answer. Frequently, answers from one part of a question are used in subsequent parts, but an error in, say, part (a), which may result in few, or even no, marks being obtained for that part should not result in no marks being obtained in subsequent parts, provided the incorrect answer is used 'correctly'. There are numbers in brackets, e.g. (3), to show how many marks are allocated to the various parts of a question.

Example 2: (a) Astronomers estimate that there are about one thousand million galaxies in the universe. Write this figure in standard form.

Answer _____ (1)

(b) Each galaxy contains about one hundred thousand million stars. Estimate the number of stars in the universe. Write your answer in standard form.

Answer _____ (2)

## Multistep questions

Sometimes the structure is not provided by the question and you must decide how to tackle the problem. There are now more of these questions in GCSE papers.

Example 3: The diagram shows the design for a company's logo which is to be painted on the side of a building.

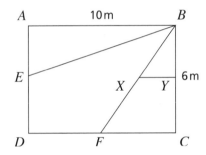

The design is a rectangle, *ABCD*, 10 m long and 6 m wide. *E*, the midpoint of *AD*, and *F*, the midpoint of *DC*, are joined to *B*. *XY* is the line joining the midpoints of *BF* and *BC*.

Calculate the area of trapezium *XYCF*.

Answer _____ m$^2$ (4)

## Non-calculator papers

From 2000, half of GCSE Mathematics papers must be answered without the use of calculating aids. Usually this means that the first paper will be non-calculator. The Mock Paper in this book has been divided into two parts. Questions in this book are shown as:

'Non-calculator'  , 'Calculator'  or 'possible on either paper'  .

## Answers to examples:

1: $x = 8$ or $x = -5$
2: (a) $1 \times 10^9$ or $10^9$    (b) $1 \times 10^{20}$ or $10^{20}$
3: Trapezium *XYCF* 11.25 m$^2$

# 1 Number

There are two main categories in Number at this level. The first, while still involving some complicated calculation, is about the effects of **errors** in measurement upon calculated results. Care is needed when computing an error to select the appropriate upper or lower bound for each variable to maximise the error.

Example 1: The value of $f$ is found from the formula $f = \dfrac{p}{q+r}$

The measurements are $p = 7.35$, $q = 15.2$, $r = 31.7$ correct to three significant figures.

(a) State the upper and lower bounds of $p$, $q$ and $r$.
(b) Find the maximum error in $f$.

Questions asked about the other category concern **rational and irrational numbers**. It is important to be clear about the definitions. Rational numbers can be written in the form of a fraction, with whole numbers in the numerator and denominator. They therefore include numbers which are terminating decimals and recurring decimals. Other numbers which cannot be written in this way, whose decimals do not terminate or recur, are irrational. Examples of these are $\sqrt{3}$ and $\pi$.

To show that a number is rational you must show that it can be written as a fraction, for example, $0.54 = \dfrac{54}{100} = \dfrac{27}{50}$

$0.\dot{5}\dot{4}$ can be shown to be a fraction by multiplying it by 100 and then subtracting. The result is $\dfrac{54}{99} = \dfrac{6}{11}$.

Example 2: Are these numbers rational or irrational? Explain your answers.

(a) $0.\dot{2}$
(b) $0.\dot{1}\dot{2}$, that is, $0.121\ 212\ldots$
(c) $0.121\ 121\ 112\ 111\ 12\ldots$

Example 3: $a = 1 + \sqrt{2}$, $b = 1 - \sqrt{2}$

Are the following rational or irrational?

$a + b, a - b, ab, a \div b$.

Give your reasons.

**If you need to revise this subject more thoroughly, see the relevant topics in the *Letts* GCSE Mathematics Study Guide or CD-ROM.**

Answers to examples:

1: (a) 7.355, 7.345; 15.25, 15.15; 31.75, 31.65

(b) 0.000 44 (i.e. 0.157 158... − 0.156 716... or 0.156 716... − 0.156 276...)

2: (a) rational: $\dfrac{1}{5}$ (b) rational: $\dfrac{12}{99} = \dfrac{4}{33}$ (c) irrational: does not recur

3: $a + b = 2$, rational;

$a - b = 2\sqrt{2}$, irrational;

$ab = -1$, rational;

$a \div b = -3 - 2\sqrt{2}$, irrational (found by multiplying top and bottom of the fraction by $(1 + \sqrt{2})$)

4

1   Angela is going to sow grass seed on a small field. She has estimated the lengths of the sides (in metres) and the angles shown in the diagram:

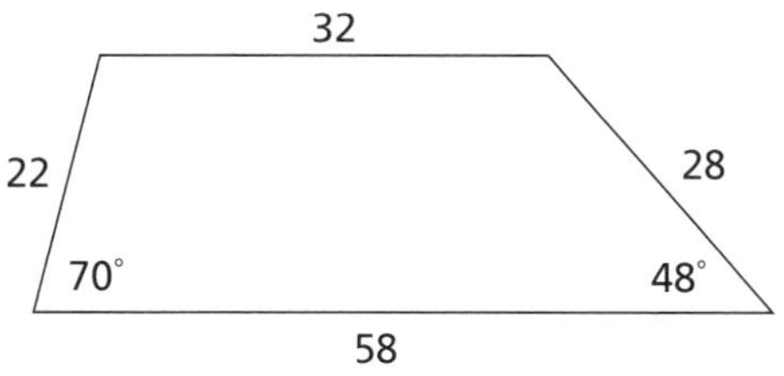

(a) Show that the field is approximately a trapezium.

   ................................................................................................................................

   ............................................................................................................... (5)

(b) All the measurements are correct to the nearest whole number. Angela has seed for 1000 m² . Can she be sure that this is enough? Show your calculation.

   ................................................................................................................................

   ............................................................................................................... (4)

2   (a) The sides of a rectangle have dimensions 20 cm and 30 cm each measured to the nearest centimetre.
      Calculate the smallest possible area of the rectangle.

      ............................................................................................................................

      ............................................................................................................................

      ............................................................................................................................

      ........................................................................................................ cm²  (2)

   (b) The sides of a square have length $x$ cm measured to the nearest centimetre.
      Write down and simplify an expression, in terms of $x$, for the difference between the largest and smallest possible areas of the square.

      ............................................................................................................................

      ............................................................................................................................

      ............................................................................................................................

      ........................................................................................................ cm²  (3)

*SEG 1998*

5

**3** (a) Write down an irrational number which lies between 4 and 5.

...................................................................................................................................... (1)

(b) $N$ is a rational number which is not equal to zero.

Show clearly why $\dfrac{1}{N}$ must also be rational.

......................................................................................................................................

...................................................................................................................................... (2)

*NEAB 1995*

**4** Kris ran a 400 m race in 49.4 seconds. If the time was measured to the nearest 0.1 seconds and the distance is measured to the nearest metre, what is the maximum value of his average speed, in metres per second?

......................................................................................................................................

......................................................................................................................................

Answer _____ m/s (3)

**5** $x$ is a number which is greater than 1.
(a) List the following four terms in order of size, smallest first.

$$x^{-2} \qquad x \qquad x^{\frac{1}{2}} \qquad \frac{1}{x}$$

......................................................................................................................................

...................................................................................................................................... (2)

(b) If $0 < x < 1$, how should your list in part (a) be rearranged, if at all?

......................................................................................................................................

...................................................................................................................................... (1)

*WJEC 1998*

**6** (a) Write down a rational number between 1.2 and 1.25.

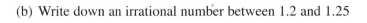 (1)

(b) Write down an irrational number between 1.2 and 1.25

_____ (1)

*Edexcel 1995*

7  (a) Show clearly that $15.4\overset{\bullet}{0}\overset{\bullet}{7}$ is a rational number.

.......................................................................................................................

....................................................................................................... (2)

(b) Given that $p = 2 + \sqrt{3}$ and $q = 2 - \sqrt{3}$, determine whether **each** of the following expressions is rational or irrational.
**All working must be shown.**

(i)  $p - q$

.............................................................................................................

.............................................................................................................

(ii) $pq$

.............................................................................................................

.............................................................................................................

(iii) $p^2$

.............................................................................................................

............................................................................................................. (6)

*WJEC 1997*

8  The diameter of a cylindrical disc of metal is measured as 28.0 mm.
   The thickness of the disc is measured as 1.9 mm.
   Four hundred of these discs are laid end-to-end in a straight line.

(a) Calculate the minimum length of the line of discs. Give your answer in metres.

.............................................................................................................

............................................................................................................. (3)

(b) Calculate the maximum possible volume of one disc in mm³.

.............................................................................................................

.............................................................................................................

............................................................................................................. (3)

*NEAB 1997*

QUESTIONS

**9** Some of these numbers are irrational. In each case, show how you decided whether it was rational or irrational.

(a) 3.142

.................................................................................................................... (1)

(b) $1.\dot{6}$

.................................................................................................................... (1)

(c) $\left(\sqrt{3}\right)^3$

.................................................................................................................... (2)

(d) $\left(1+\sqrt{3}\right)\left(1-\sqrt{3}\right)$

.................................................................................................................... (2)

(e) $\dfrac{1+\sqrt{3}}{1-\sqrt{3}}$

.................................................................................................................... (3)

**10** David travels from Manchester to London in $3\frac{1}{2}$ hours, measured to the nearest half hour.

The distance from Manchester to London is 200 miles, measured to the nearest 10 miles.

(a) Complete these two inequalities:

3.25 hours < David's time < _____

_____ < Distance from Manchester to London < _____ (3)

(b) Calculate upper and lower bounds for the average speed for David's journey.

Give these bounds correct to 3 significant figures where appropriate.

....................................................................................................................

....................................................................................................................

Answer   Upper bound _____ mph

Lower bound _____ mph   (4)

*MEG 1995*

There is an increasing emphasis on the manipulation of algebraic expressions and the solution of equations in GCSE papers.

Example 1: Simplify $\dfrac{1}{x-2} + \dfrac{1}{2x+3}$

Example 2: Solve the equation $3x^2 - 2x - 7 = 0$.
Give the solutions correct to 4 significant figures.

The last part of this section is concerned with graphs. You may be asked
- to solve equations by graphical means;
- find the gradients of curves by drawing tangents;
- find the area under a curve and explain its significance;
- sketch graphs of functions.

Example 3: This is the graph of $y = f(x)$.

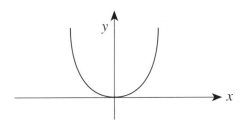

Sketch the graphs of $y = f(x + 1)$, $y = f(x) + 1$.

Answers to examples:

1: $\dfrac{3x+1}{(x-2)(2x+3)}$

2: $x = 1.897$ or $-1.230$

3:

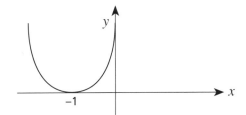

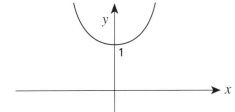

> **If you need to revise this subject more thoroughly, see the relevant topics in the *Letts* GCSE Mathematics Study Guide or CD-ROM.**

**1**   $1, \quad 2, \quad 1\frac{1}{2}, \quad 1\frac{3}{4}, \quad 1\frac{5}{8}, \quad ...$

(a) Explain how to get the next term.

............................................................................................................................................. (1)

(b) Investigate whether or not this sequence converges and, if it does, find the limit.

.........................................................................................................................................

.........................................................................................................................................

.........................................................................................................................................

Answer _____ (4)

**2**   Pipes with equal diameters are arranged in a stack.

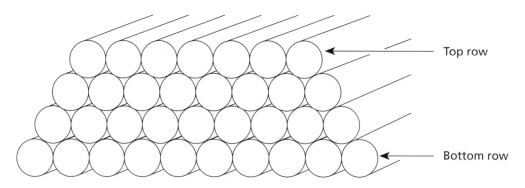

Top row

Bottom row

To find the number of pipes, $P$, in a stack, the following formula can be used

$$P = \frac{(b+a)(b-a+1)}{2}$$

where $b$ is the number of pipes on the bottom row and $a$ is the number of pipes on the top row.

(a) Use this formula to find the number of pipes in a stack where $b = 40$ and $a = 15$.

............................................................................................................................................. (1)

(b) In a particular stack, the number of pipes on the bottom row is twice the number on the top row.

Show that in this stack $P = \dfrac{3a^2 + 3a}{2}$ where $a$ is the number of pipes on the top row.

.........................................................................................................................................

.........................................................................................................................................

............................................................................................................................................. (3)

(c) Would it be possible to arrange exactly 975 pipes in the kind of stack described in part (b)? **Justify your answer**.

..............................................................................................................................

..............................................................................................................................

.................................................................................................................. (3)

*SQA 1995*

**3** Freda wants to make a run for her rabbits. She has a roll of netting 22 m long and is going to use it to make three sides of a rectangle. The other side will be part of the garden fence. The length of the side at right angles to the fence is $x$ m. The area inside will be 60 m².

(a) Show that $x^2 - 11x + 30 = 0$.

.................................................................................................................. (3)

(b) Solve the equation.

..............................................................................................................................

..............................................................................................................................

Answer  $x =$ _____ (3)

(c) Describe the size of the run.

.................................................................................................................. (2)

**4** (a) Simplify the following expression

$$\sqrt{\frac{2a^3b^2 \times 4a^2b^{\frac{1}{2}}}{8a^2b \times 9ab^2}}.$$

...........................................................................................................................

...........................................................................................................................

Answer _____ (2)

(b) Rearrange this equation $s = \frac{1}{2}at^2$ to give $t$ in terms of $s$.

...........................................................................................................................

Answer $t =$ _____ (2)

(c) Simplify the following expression

$$\frac{3x^2 - 2x - 1}{x^2 - 1}.$$

...........................................................................................................................

...........................................................................................................................

...........................................................................................................................

...........................................................................................................................

Answer _____ (2)

**5** Mr Brick the builder owns a plot of land, *ABCD*. The dimensions are in metres.

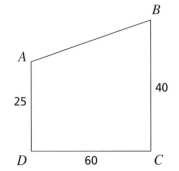

Not to scale

He decides that it is big enough for two houses. He wants to divide it so that the areas of the two parts are equal. The dividing line *EF* must be parallel to *AD* and *BC*. *DF* = *x*.

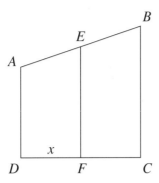

(a) Explain why $EF = 25 + \frac{1}{4}x$.

.............................................................................................................................. (2)

(b) Show that *x* satisfies the equation

$$x^2 + 200x - 7800 = 0.$$

..............................................................................................................................

.............................................................................................................................. (3)

(c) Solve the equation to find the length of *DF*. Give your answer to the nearest 0.1 m.

..............................................................................................................................

..............................................................................................................................

Answer  *x* = _____ (3)

(d) Explain how you know your answer is about right.

.............................................................................................................................. (1)

**6** (a) Simplify the expression:

$$\frac{2x^2 - 5x + 2}{x^2 - 4}$$

..............................................................................................................................

..............................................................................................................................

..............................................................................................................................

Answer  _____ (3)

(b) The expression $x^2 - 8x + 17$ can be written in the form $(x - p)^2 + q$.
Calculate the values of $p$ and $q$ such that
$$x^2 - 8x + 17 = (x - p)^2 + q.$$

....................................................................................................................

....................................................................................................................

....................................................................................................................

Answer $p = $ _____ (1)

Answer $q = $ _____ (1)

*SEG 1998*

**7** The area of a rectangle is 6 m². If the diagonal is $\sqrt{13}$ m long what are the dimensions of the rectangle?

....................................................................................................................

....................................................................................................................

Answer _____ m by _____ m (6)

**8** A glass was filled with boiling water and was then left to cool for three hours. The graph below shows the temperature of the water after $t$ minutes.

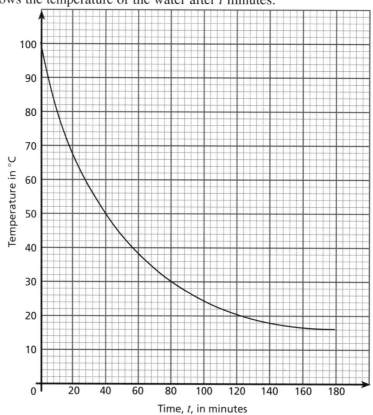

(a) Draw the tangent to the curve at the point where $t = 80$. (1)

(b) Find the gradient of the curve at the point where $t = 80$ and state its units.

...................................................................................................................................

Answer   Gradient = _____

Units _____ (3)

(c) What does the gradient of this graph measure?

................................................................................................................... (1)

*MEG 1995*

**9**   These are the stopping distances for cars at various speeds on a dry road:

| Speed ($s$ miles/hour) | 30 | 50 | 70 |
|---|---|---|---|
| Stopping distance ($d$ feet) | 75 | 175 | 315 |

There is a formula connecting $d$ and $s$.

(a) Show that it is not linear.

...................................................................................................................................

................................................................................................................... (1)

(b) Show that $d$ is not proportional to $s^2$.

...................................................................................................................................

................................................................................................................... (1)

(c) The formula is $d = ts + ks^2$. Find the values of $t$ and $k$.

...................................................................................................................................

...................................................................................................................................

Answer   $t = $ _____   $k = $ _____ (5)

**10** Write these expressions as simply as possible, using index notation:

(a) $x \sqrt{x}$             (b) $\dfrac{1}{x^2}$             (c) $(x^3 y^2)^2$

...................................................................................................................................

...................................................................................................................................

Answer (a) _____ (b) _____ (c) _____   (3)

**11**

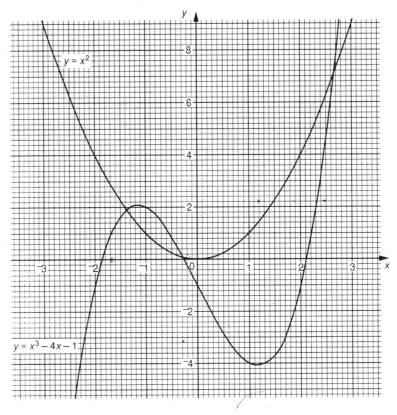

Use the graphs drawn to solve these equations.

(a) $x^2 = x^3 - 4x - 1$

  (1)

(b) $x^3 - 4x - 1 = 1$

  (2)

(c) By drawing a suitable straight line on the graph, solve the equation $x^3 - 5x + 1 = 0$.

...............................................................................................................................

...............................................................................................................................

............................................................................................................ (4)

*MEG 1997*

**12**

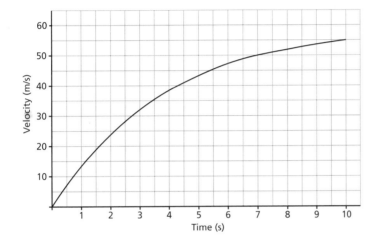

This graph shows the velocity of a sports car starting from rest.

(a) Find the acceleration at time $t = 4$. State the units in your answer.

...............................................................................................................................

Answer _____ (3)

(b) Estimate how far the car has travelled during the first 10 seconds.
Make your method clear.

...............................................................................................................................

Answer _____ m (4)

**13** The diagram shows the cross section of part of a river bed. *AB* is the water surface.
The units are metres.

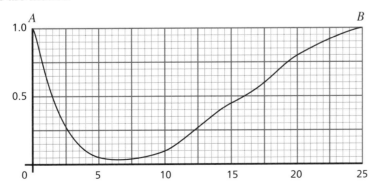

Find the area of cross section.

......................................................................................................................................

......................................................................................................................................

Answer _____ m$^2$  (3)

**14** The graph of $y = f(x)$ where $f(x) = \dfrac{x}{x+1}$ is sketched below.

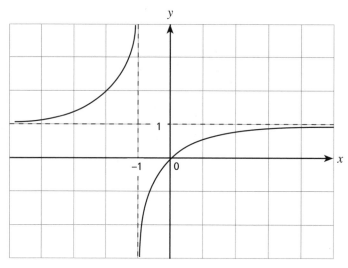

Hence, or otherwise, sketch on the axis below

(a) $y = f(x - 1)$

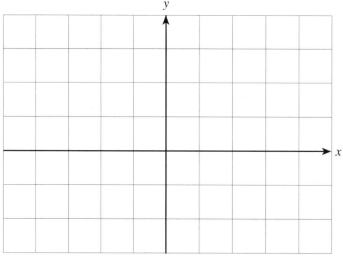

(2)

(b) $y = f(2x)$

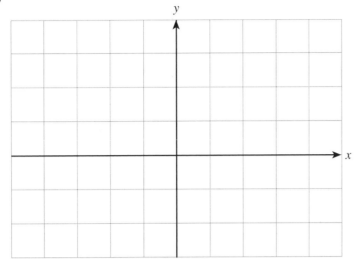

(2)

*SEG 1995*

**15** The sketch shows the graph of the function

$$y = f(x).$$

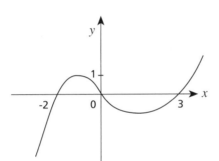

On the diagrams below, sketch the graphs of:

$y = f(x) + 2$                     $y = f(x + 2)$

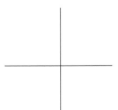       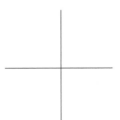

$y = f(x) - 3$                     $y = f(x - 3)$

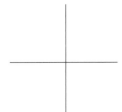       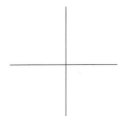

(4)

**16** This is part of the graph of $y = x^3 - 3x$.

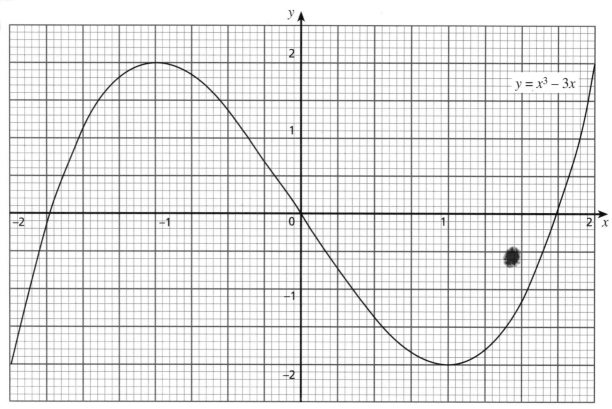

(a) Use the graph to solve the equation

$$x^3 - 3x = 1.$$

.............................................................................................................................

Answer $x =$ _____ (2)

(b) By drawing a suitable straight line, solve the equation

$$x^3 - 2x = 1.$$

.............................................................................................................................

Answer $x =$ _____ (3)

**17** Solve the inequality

$$(x + 3)^2 < x^2 + 2x + 7$$

Do **not** use a trial and improvement method.

.................................................................................................................................

.................................................................................................................................

.................................................................................................................................

................................................................................................................ (3)

*NEAB 1998*

**18** Solve the following equation.

$$\frac{2}{x + 2} + \frac{3}{2x - 1} = 1$$

.................................................................................................................................

.................................................................................................................................

.................................................................................................................................

.................................................................................................................................

.................................................................................................................................

.................................................................................................................................

.................................................................................................................................

.................................................................................................................................

.................................................................................................................................

................................................................................................................ (7)

*WJEC 1998*

Solution of problems in more **complicated 2-D and 3-D** situations will be required by some questions in this attainment target. In solid shapes you will need to locate suitable plane sections in order to find the necessary angles and distances.

Example 1:

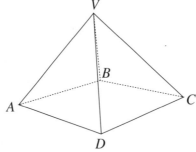

All the edges of this square-based pyramid are length 5 cm.
(a) Find the angle between $VC$ and the base. (Use triangle $VAC$.)
(b) Find the angle between $VCD$ and the base. (Use the triangle in the plane bisecting $CD$ through $V$.)

Calculations will also be asked for in triangles which do not contain right angles. Here the **cosine rule** or the **sine rule** can be used.

Example 2: Find the length of $QR$ and the size of the other angles in this triangle.

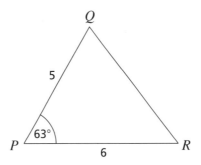

There may also be questions on combining transformations.

Example 3: An object is reflected in $x = 0$ and the result is reflected in $y = 0$.

Describe the single transformation that is equivalent to this.

The last type of question is on vectors, either describing a physical situation, such as a resultant force, or purely in geometry, as in this example.

Example 4: $\mathbf{a} = \begin{pmatrix} 1 \\ 2 \end{pmatrix}$, $\mathbf{b} = \begin{pmatrix} -3 \\ 0 \end{pmatrix}$. Find $2\mathbf{a} - \mathbf{b}$.

If you need to revise this subject more thoroughly, see the relevant topics in the *Letts* GCSE *Mathematics Study Guide* or CD-ROM.

Answers to examples:

1: (a) 45°          (b) 54.7°
2: $QR = 5.81$; angle $PRQ = 50.1°$; angle $PQR = 66.9°$
3: Half turn about the origin.
4: $\begin{pmatrix} 5 \\ 4 \end{pmatrix}$

**1** How many spherical balls of radius 1 cm can be made from a large spherical ball of 3 cm radius?

..............................................................................................................................................

..............................................................................................................................................

Answer _____ (2)

**2** A lampshade is made by removing the top *VCA* from a hollow cone *VDB* of height 36 cm as shown. The diameter *DB* at the base of the cone is 30 cm and the diameter, *AC*, of the base of the cone removed is 10 cm.

(a) Find the height *h* of the lampshade.

..............................................................................................................................................

..............................................................................................................................................

..............................................................................................................................................

Answer _____ cm (3)

(b) Find the area of the material needed to cover the lampshade.

..............................................................................................................................................

..............................................................................................................................................

..............................................................................................................................................

Answer _____ cm$^2$ (6)

*Area of curved surface of a cone = πrl*

**3** The diagram below represents a rolling pin made from three pieces of wood.
The central part of the rolling pin is a cylinder of length 20.5 cm and radius 2.5 cm.
The handles are cylindrical with hemispherical ends.
The cylindrical handles and their hemispherical ends each have a radius of 0.5 cm.
The total length of the rolling pin is 40.5 cm.

*Diagram not drawn to scale*

(a) Calculate the total volume of the rolling pin.

.......................................................................................................................................

.......................................................................................................................................

.......................................................................................................................................

.......................................................................................................................................

.......................................................................................................................................

....................................................................................................................... (7)

(b) Another wooden rolling pin is **similar** to this rolling pin but all its dimensions are 1.2 times larger. Using the answer to *(a)*, calculate the volume of the larger rolling pin.

.......................................................................................................................................

.......................................................................................................................................

....................................................................................................................... (2)

*WJEC 1998*

**4** Triangle *ABC* and vectors **a** and **b** are shown on the grid.

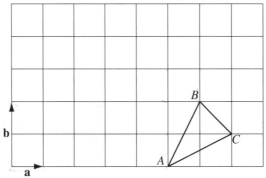

(a) Draw the position of the triangle *ABC* after translation by the vector **b** − 2**a**. (1)

(b) (i) Write the vector $\vec{AB}$ in terms of **a** and **b**.

Answer $\vec{AB}$ = _____ (1)

(ii) Write the vector $\vec{BC}$ ; in terms of **a** and **b**.

Answer $\vec{BC}$ = _____ (1)

(c) $D$ is an unmarked point on the grid.

$$\vec{BD} = \frac{2}{3}\,\vec{BC} \;.$$

$$\vec{AD} = x\mathbf{a} + y\mathbf{b}.$$

Use your answers to (b) to **calculate** the values of $x$ and $y$.
You **must** show all your working.

.............................................................................................................................

.............................................................................................................................

.............................................................................................................................

Answers: $x =$ _____ $y =$ _____ (4)

*SEG 1998*

**5** A model power boat can travel at 0.75 m/s in still water. It is released from a point $P$ on the bank of a river which flows at 0.4 m/s. The river is 15 m wide. The boat is aimed continually in a direction perpendicular to the flow of the river, as shown in the diagram.

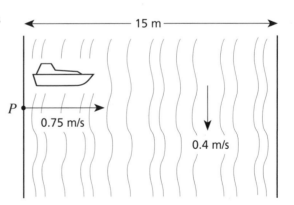

(a) By scale drawing or by calculation, find

(i) the resultant speed of the boat; (2)

(ii) the direction in which the boat actually travels across the river. (2)

Answers: (i) _____ (ii) _____

(b) (i) How far downstream from *P* does the boat land on the opposite bank?

.......................................................................................................... (2)

(ii) How long does the boat take to cross the river?

.......................................................................................................... (2)

*NEAB 1995*

**6** Find the heights of these isosceles triangles.

(a)

.............................................................................

.............................................................................

.............................................................................

.............................................................................

Answer _____ (4)

(b)

.............................................................................

.............................................................................

.............................................................................

.............................................................................

Answer _____ (3)

(c)

.............................................................................

.............................................................................

.............................................................................

Answer _____ (6)

**7** This is Shirley's garden shed.
It is 2.5 m long.

2.5 m

Here are the plan and elevations of the shed:

(a) What is the scale of the plan?

Answer _____ (1)

(b) How high is the shed?

...............................................................................................................

Answer _____ m  (1)

(c) Shirley has a pole 3.25 m long.
She tries to put it in the shed as shown:

Use calculation to see whether it will fit.

...............................................................................................................

............................................................................................................... (3)

27

(d) Find the length of the longest pole that will fit into the shed in any position.

.......................................................................................................................

.......................................................................................................................

.......................................................................................................................

Answer _____ m (5)

**8** 4 cylindrical rods, each of radius 1 cm are packed into a cylindrical container as shown below. (The centres of the rods are at the corners of a square.)

Calculate the radius of the container.

.......................................................................................................................

.......................................................................................................................

.......................................................................................................................

Answer _____ cm (5)

**9** The depth of water in the harbour at St Nazaire is given by the formula

$$D = L + K\sin(29.2t)°$$

where $L - K$ is the depth at low tide
$L + K$ is the depth at high tide
$t$ is the time in hours since midnight on 1 July.

(a) At what time is the first high tide on 1 July?

.......................................................................................................................

Answer _____ (2)

(b) At what time is the first low tide on 1 July?

.......................................................................................................................

Answer _____ (2)

(c) Is the depth of water in the harbour more or less at midnight on 2 July than at midnight on 1 July? Show how you decided.

..................................................................................................................................

Answer _____ (2)

(d) Is the tide rising or falling at midnight on 5 July? Show how you decided.

..................................................................................................................................

Answer _____ (3)

**10** Figure 1 shows a road bridge.

**Figure 1**

The curved part of the bridge is formed from an arc of a circle, centre O, as shown in Figure 2.

**Figure 2**

*OA* and *OB* are radii of length 170 metres.

The height of the middle of the bridge above its ends is 28 metres as shown in Figure 2.

Calculate the horizontal distance, *AB*.

**Do not use a scale drawing.**

..................................................................................................................................

.......................................................................................................................... (4)

*SQA 1995*

QUESTIONS

**11** A ladder leans against the semi-circular roof of a barn as shown.
E is the centre of the semi-circle.
Angle BDF = 60°.
All lengths shown are in metres.

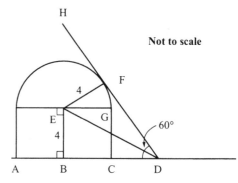

Not to scale

(a) Explain carefully why triangles EBD and EFD are congruent.

........................................................................................................................

........................................................................................................................

(b) Calculate the length BD.

........................................................................................................................

(c) The top end of the ladder, H, is vertically above point B.
Calculate the length of the ladder.

........................................................................................................................ (7)

*MEG 1997*

**12** This picture shows a goods van as used on the Welshpool and Llanfair Railway.

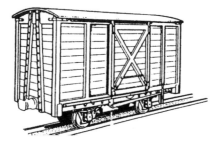

This diagram shows one end.

The roof is a circular arc, centre *B*.
*RP* = 2.10 m, *PQ* = 2.33 m.

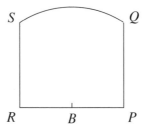

(a) Calculate   (i) the length of *BQ*,

........................................................................................................................

Answer _____ m  (2)

(ii) the angle *BQP*,

..................................................................................................................................

Answer _____ ° (3)

(iii) the length of the arc *QS*.

..................................................................................................................................

Answer _____ cm (3)

(b) Calculate the area of the end *RSQP*.

..................................................................................................................................

..................................................................................................................................

Answer _____ m$^2$ (4)

Penelope has made a model of the van to a scale $\frac{1}{19}$.

(c) (i) How wide is the model?

..................................................................................................................................

Answer _____ cm (1)

(ii) What is the area of the end of the model?

..................................................................................................................................

Answer _____ cm$^2$ (2)

**13** *A*, *B*, *C* and *D* are four points on the circumference of a circle centre *0*.
The tangent *FG* meets the circle at *C*.
Angle *BCF* = 72° and angle *ABC* = 50°.

*Not drawn to scale*

Find **each** of the following angles.

(a) Angle *AOC* ...........................................................................................................

..................................................................................................................................

(b) Angle *ADC* ............................................................................................................

..................................................................................................................................

(c) Angle *BAC* .............................................................................................................

..................................................................................................................................

(d) Angle *OAB* ............................................................................................................

..................................................................................................................................

.................................................................................................................... (5)

*WJEC 1998*

**14** A wiper blade on a windscreen cleans the shaded area as shown.

110°□

16cm      42cm      *Not drawn to scale*

Calculate the area of the windsreen cleaned by the wiper.

..................................................................................................................................

..................................................................................................................................

..................................................................................................................................

..................................................................................................................................

..................................................................................................................................

Answer _____ cm² (4)

*SEG 1998*

**15** ABCD is the rectangular base of a pyramid with vertex V. V is **not** directly over the centre of the base. The measurements in the diagram are in centimetres.

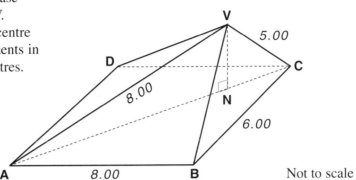

Not to scale

Calculate

(a) AC,

...................................................................................................

...................................................................................................

...................................................................................................

Answer AC = _____ cm

(b) the angle AVC,

...................................................................................................

...................................................................................................

...................................................................................................

Answer angle AVC = _____ °

(c) The height of the pyramid, VN.
Give your answer correct to two decimal places.

...................................................................................................

...................................................................................................

...................................................................................................

................................................................................................... (8)

Answer VN = _____ cm

*MEG 1996*

**16** A ship, *A*, is 9.2 km from a port, *P*, on a bearing N37°E (037°).
Another ship, *B*, is 4.5 km from *P* on a bearing S63°E (117°).

*Diagram not drawn to scale*

(a) Calculate the distance, *AB*, between the two ships.

......................................................................................................................................

......................................................................................................................................

......................................................................................................................................

......................................................................................................................................

...................................................................................................................... (3)

(b) Calculate the bearing of ship *A* from ship *B*. Give your answer to the nearest degree.

......................................................................................................................................

......................................................................................................................................

......................................................................................................................................

......................................................................................................................................

......................................................................................................................................

...................................................................................................................... (3)

*WJEC 1998*

There will be questions in this section about **collecting, processing and interpreting data.**

   Calculations to find measures of central tendency and spread will be required, such as the mean and standard deviation. It is useful here to have a calculator which has these functions and to learn how to use it. Histograms may be drawn for frequency distributions where the frequency is represented by the area under the histogram, not by the heights of the columns. The axis up the page will be *frequency density*.

Example 1:  The table shows the frequency distribution of the heights of 50 girls in a primary school.

(a) Calculate estimates of the mean and standard deviation.
(b) Complete the frequency density column.

| Height ($x$ cm) | Frequency | Frequency density |
|---|---|---|
| $95 \leqslant x < 105$ | 7 | |
| $105 \leqslant x < 115$ | 13 | |
| $115 \leqslant x < 120$ | 14 | |
| $120 \leqslant x < 125$ | 8 | |
| $125 \leqslant x < 145$ | 8 | |

   The last topic in this section is **probability**. Many of the situations which you will be asked about will involve conditional probability, where the probabilities are different depending on what happens before the event, such as:

Example 2:  The probability that it will rain today is 0.6.
             If it rains today, the probability that it will rain tomorrow is 0.4.
             If it is fine today, the probability that it will be fine tomorrow is 0.7.
             What is the probability that just one of the two days will be wet?

If you need to revise this subject more thoroughly, see the relevant topics in the *Letts* GCSE *Mathematics Study Guide* or CD-ROM.

Answers to examples:

1: (a) mean = 116.7, standard deviation = 10.5
   (b) Frequency density: 0.7, 1.3, 2.8, 1.6, 0.4
2: 0.48

**QUESTIONS**

**1**   In a survey 50 people were asked how many hours of television they watched in one week. The histogram shows the results of the survey.

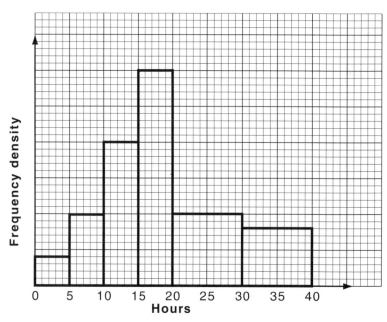

No one watched more than 40 hours of television in one week.

(a)  Use the histogram to complete the table of values.

| Number of hours | 0– | 5– | 10– | 15– | 20– | 30–40 |
|---|---|---|---|---|---|---|
| Frequency | 2 | | | | | |

........................................................................................................................................

.................................................................................................................... (3)

(b)  The survey was carried out by questioning the first 50 people who went into a shop after 10.00 on a Thursday morning.

(i)  Give one reason why this sample may not be representative of the population.

........................................................................................................................................

.................................................................................................................... (1)

(ii) Suggest a better way of ensuring that the sample is representative of the population.

........................................................................................................................................

.................................................................................................................... (1)

*SEG 1996*

2  The West Albion Garden Society has tested two brands of fertiliser for growing marrows. Unfortunately the groupings are different and the results difficult to compare.

| BRAND A | |
|---|---|
| Mass in kg | Frequency |
| Less than 0.5 | 1 |
| $\geqslant 0.5$ and $< 1.0$ | 7 |
| $\geqslant 1.0$ and $< 2.5$ | 12 |
| $\geqslant 2.5$ and $< 5.0$ | 10 |
| $\geqslant 5.0$ and $< 10$ | 3 |

| BRAND B | |
|---|---|
| Mass in kg | Frequency |
| Less than 1.0 | 4 |
| $\geqslant 1.0$ and $< 2.0$ | 4 |
| $\geqslant 2.0$ and $< 3.0$ | 6 |
| $\geqslant 3.0$ and $< 4.0$ | 6 |
| $\geqslant 4.0$ and $< 5.0$ | 7 |
| $\geqslant 5.0$ and $< 10$ | 3 |

(a) Draw the histograms.

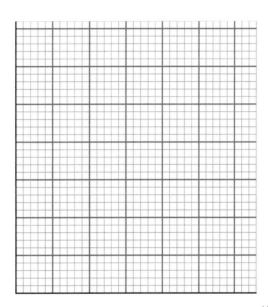

(6)

(b) Calculate estimates of the mean and standard deviation for each brand.

........................................................................................................................................

........................................................................................................................................

Answers

| | | | |
|---|---|---|---|
| A | Mean: | | SD: |
| B | Mean: | | SD: |

(5)

(c) Compare the results.

.................................................................................................................... (2)

QUESTIONS

**3** A bag contains 4 red balls, 5 green balls and 3 yellow balls.
Two balls are selected at random without replacement from the bag.
Calculate the probability that

(a) both balls are yellow,

..........................................................................................................................

..........................................................................................................................

.................................................................................................................. (3)

(b) the two balls have different colours.

..........................................................................................................................

..........................................................................................................................

.................................................................................................................. (4)

*WJEC 1998*

**4** Sam was making a survey of pupils in his school.

He wanted to find out their opinions on noise pollution by motor bikes.

The size of each year group in the school is shown below.

| Year group | Boys | Girls | Total |
|---|---|---|---|
| 8 | 85 | 65 | 150 |
| 9 | 72 | 75 | 147 |
| 10 | 74 | 78 | 152 |
| 11 | 77 | 72 | 149 |
| 6th Form | 93 | 107 | 200 |
| | | | 798 |

Sam took a sample of 80 pupils.

(a) Explain whether or not he should have sampled equal numbers of boys and girls in year 8.

.................................................................................................................. (1)

(b) Calculate the number of pupils he should have sampled in year 8.

..........................................................................................................................

Answer _____ (3)

*Edexcel 1995*

**5** A canteen offers a choice of main course and sweet. For each course one of two choices must be selected.

The tree diagram below shows the choices that a customer can make, and some of the probabilities of those choices.

(a) Complete the tree diagram.

```
        Main Course           Sweet
                                    Fruit
                Roast beef
                           0.8
                                    Ice cream
         0.4
                                    Fruit
                Vegetarian
                            0.8
                                    Ice cream                    (1)
```

(b) Work out the probability that a customer chooses roast beef and ice cream.

..................................................................................................

..................................................................................................

Answer _____ (2)

Experience has shown that the choices are not independent of one another.

If a customer chooses roast beef the probability of choosing fruit is 0.3 but if they choose vegetarian then the probability of choosing fruit is only 0.1.

The probability of choosing vegetarian stays at 0.4.

(c) Show these revised probabilities on the tree diagram below.

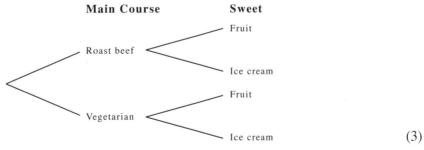

(3)

(d) Using your tree diagram from (c), calculate the probability that a customer chooses ice cream for sweet.

..................................................................................................

..................................................................................................

Answer _____ (3)

*SEG 1996*

**QUESTIONS**

**6** The heights of a group of 310 pupils are recorded in the table.

| Height | Number of pupils |
|---|---|
| up to but not including 120 cm | 0 |
| 120 cm up to but not including 140 cm | 80 |
| 140 cm up to but not including 150 cm | 60 |
| 150 cm up to but not including 160 cm | 70 |
| 160 cm up to but not including 165 cm | 40 |
| 165 cm up to but not including 180 cm | 60 |
| 180 cm or more | 0 |

Complete the histogram on the grid below.

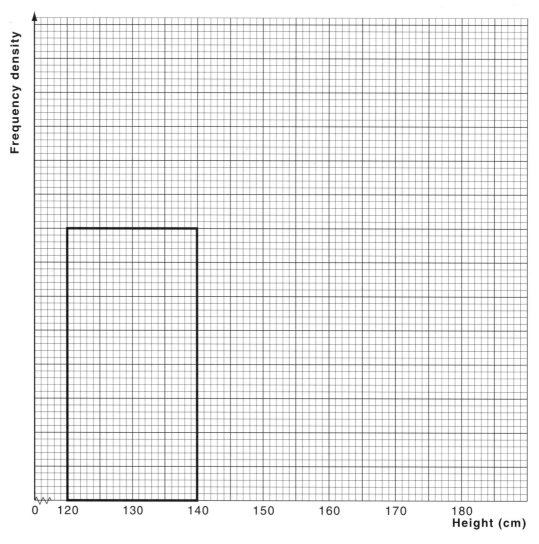

(4)

7  In the game of tennis a player has two serves.

If the first serve is successful the game continues.

If the first serve is not successful the player serves again. If this second service is successful the game continues.

If both serves are unsuccessful the player has served a 'double fault' and loses the point.

Gabriella plays tennis. She is successful with 60% of her first serves and 95% of her second serves.

(a) Calculate the probability that Gabriella serves a double fault.

..............................................................................................................................

..............................................................................................................................

..............................................................................................................................

..............................................................................................................................

..............................................................................................................................

Answer (a) _____ (3)

If Gabriella is successful with her first serve she has a probability of 0.75 of winning the point.

If she is successful with her second serve she has a probability of 0.5 of winning the point.

(b) Calculate the probability that Gabriella wins the point.

..............................................................................................................................

..............................................................................................................................

..............................................................................................................................

..............................................................................................................................

..............................................................................................................................

..............................................................................................................................

..............................................................................................................................

Answer (b) _____ (4)

*MEG 1996*

**8** Malcolm is playing a game with three ordinary dice, faces numbered 1, 2, 3, 4, 5, 6.
He throws each in turn. He wins the game if any one shows a six.

(a) (i) Complete the tree diagram.

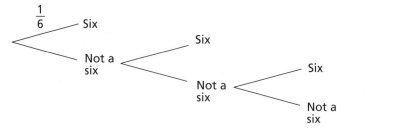

(2)

(ii) What is the probability that he wins with the second throw?

..........................................................................................................................

Answer _____ (2)

(iii) What is the probability that he wins?

..........................................................................................................................

Answer _____ (3)

Veronica is playing another game with six cards numbered 1, 2, 3, 4, 5, 6. She takes a card at random and does not replace it. If it is a six she wins. If not, she draws another card, again not replacing it. If it is a six she wins. If not, a third card is drawn. If it is a six she wins.

(b) (i) Complete the tree diagram.

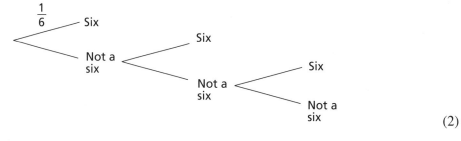

(2)

(ii) What is the probability that she wins with the second draw?

..........................................................................................................................

Answer _____ (2)

(iii) What is the probability that she wins?

..........................................................................................................................

Answer _____ (3)

(iv) Explain how you could have found the answer to (iii) another way.

.......................................................................................................................... (1)

**9** Students finishing a word-processing course had their speeds measured in characters per minute (ch/min) with the following results.

| Speed (in ch/min) | Number of students |
|---|---|
| 100 — | 20 |
| 300 — | 34 |
| 350 — | 40 |
| 400 — | 32 |
| 450 — | 28 |
| 500 — | 12 |
| 600 and over | 0 |

Using these axes, draw a histogram to display these data                                          (4)

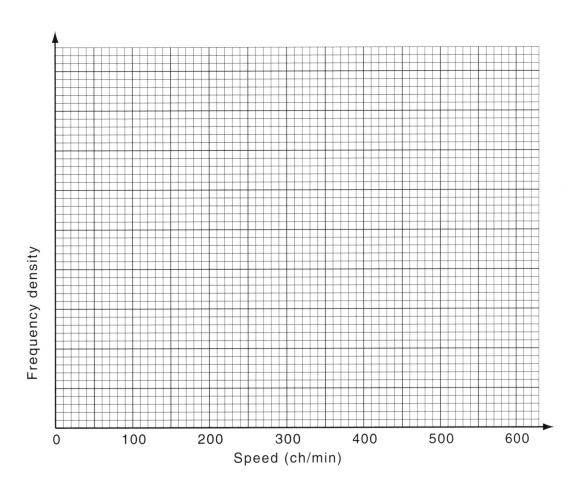

*MEG 1996*

**10** One hundred schools in the north of England and one hundred in the south take part in a national 'weather watch' project. As part of the project they record the rainfall at their school for the month of May.

The histogram below shows the distribution of rainfall for schools in the north of England.

**May rainfall recorded by one hundred schools in the north of England**

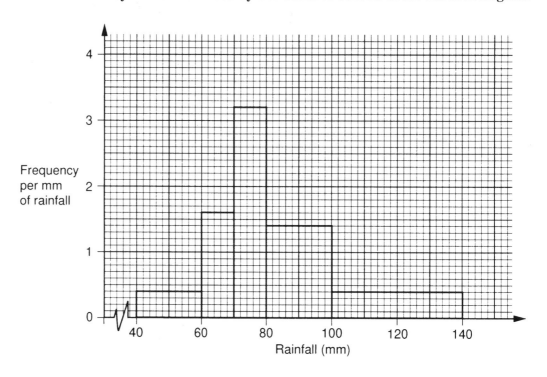

(a) (i)  Use the histogram to find the number of schools which recorded between 60 and 70 mm of rain during May.

..........................................................................................................................................

.................................................................................................................. (1)

(ii)  Use the histogram to find the number of schools which recorded more than 80 mm of rain during May.

..........................................................................................................................................

.................................................................................................................. (2)

The table below shows the rainfall recorded by the one hundred schools in the south of England.

| Rainfall ($x$ mm) | $40 < x \leqslant 50$ | $50 < x \leqslant 60$ | $60 < x \leqslant 70$ | $70 < x \leqslant 90$ | $90 < x \leqslant 140$ |
|---|---|---|---|---|---|
| Frequency | 11 | 38 | 27 | 14 | 10 |

(b) Complete the histogram below to display this information.

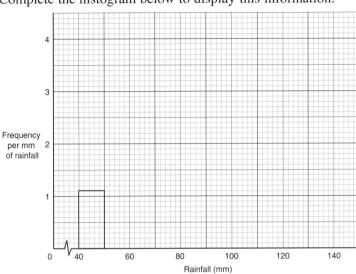

(5)

(c) Examine the two histograms and make **three** comparisons between the May rainfall in the north and south of England.

1 ................................................................................................................................

................................................................................................................................

2 ................................................................................................................................

................................................................................................................................

3 ................................................................................................................................

................................................................................................................ (3)

*MEG 1997*

**11** Ceri is training for a swimming competition. During a training session, she swims 50 lengths of a swimming pool and her trainer records the time she takes to complete each length. A summary of the times, in seconds, is recorded in the grouped frequency distribution below.

| Time<br>$t$ seconds | Frequency<br>$f$ | Frequency<br>density |
|---|---|---|
| $85 \leqslant t < 90$ | 5 | |
| $90 \leqslant t < 95$ | 9 | |
| $95 \leqslant t < 105$ | 21 | |
| $105 \leqslant t < 115$ | 11 | |
| $115 \leqslant t \leqslant 120$ | 4 | |

(a) Complete the frequency density column. (1)

QUESTIONS

(b) On the graph paper below, draw a histogram of the distribution of the times taken by Ceri to swim a length of the pool.

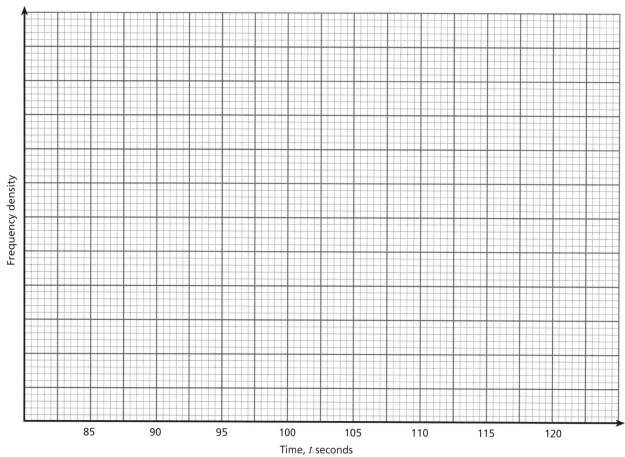

Time, *t* seconds

(3)

(c) The times, in seconds, that Ceri took to complete the first 10 lengths were 93, 90, 87, 85, 86, 86, 92, 94, 90, and 92. The mean time for these ten lengths is 89.5 seconds. Find the standard deviation of the times, in seconds, of the first ten lengths, giving your answer correct to one decimal place.

........................................................................................................................

........................................................................................................ (2)

(d) Use your histogram to estimate the proportion of lengths, in the whole training session, which took longer than 110 seconds.

........................................................................................................................

........................................................................................................ (2)

*WJEC 1995*

**12** The committee of St Minnack & Porthcumo Youth Club consists of 3 boys and 5 girls. At the AGM. the secretary and the treasurer are chosen at random from the committee members. The secretary is chosen first.

(a) What is the probability that one particular boy, Darren, will be chosen as secretary?

..................................................................................................................

.......................................................................................................... (1)

One of the rules of the Club is that the secretary and the treasurer must be of different sexes. (For example, if a boy is chosen as secretary, then the treasurer is chosen at random from the girls.)

(b) Before either the secretary or the treasurer is chosen, what is the probability that one particular girl, Tamarin, will be chosen as treasurer?

..................................................................................................................

.......................................................................................................... (2)

(c) Bryn and his sister Gwyneth are two members of the committee.

(i) Find the probability that Bryn will be chosen as secretary and Gwyneth as treasurer.

.......................................................................................................... (1)

(ii) Find the probability that one of them will be chosen as secretary and the other as treasurer.

..................................................................................................................

.......................................................................................................... (3)

*MEG 1996*

**13** Ten boys sat a test which was marked out of 50.
Their marks were 28, 42, 35, 17, 49, 12, 48, 38, 24 and 27.

(a) Calculate

(i) the mean of the marks,

.......................................................................................................... (2)

(ii) the standard deviation of the marks.

.......................................................................................................... (2)

Ten girls sat the same test.
Their marks had a mean of 30 and a standard deviation of 6.5.

(b) Compare the performances of the boys and girls.

.......................................................................................................... (2)

*NEAB 1995*

**14** How many times must you toss a fair coin for the probability of getting at least one head to be more than 0.95?

.......................................................................................................................

.......................................................................................................................

Answer _____ (5)

**15** In a particular college, the probability that a student is a vegetarian is 0.35 and the probability that a student lives in self-catering accommodation is 0.57. The probability that a student is a vegetarian and lives in self-catering accommodation is 0.15.

Calculate the probability that a student selected at random

(a) is a vegetarian or lives in self-catering accommodation or both,

.......................................................................................................................

.......................................................................................................................

....................................................................................................................... (3)

(b) is not a vegetarian and does not live in self-catering accommodation,

.......................................................................................................................

.......................................................................................................................

....................................................................................................................... (2)

(c) is a vegetarian but does not live in self-catering accommodation.

.......................................................................................................................

.......................................................................................................................

....................................................................................................................... (2)

*WJEC 1997*

*Time 2 hours, 100 marks available.*

**Section A** *Do not use a calculator.*

1  (a) Astronomers believe that there are about one thousand million galaxies in the universe and that each galaxy contains about one hundred thousand million stars.
What is the approximate number of stars in the universe?
Give your answer in standard form.

..................................................................................................................................... (2)

   (b) The land area of the Earth's surface is about $4 \times 10^{11}\,\mathrm{km^2}$.
The population of the Earth is approximately 5000 million.
Approximately what is the average area, in $\mathrm{km^2}$, per head of the population?

..................................................................................................................................... (2)

2  In the following formulas, $a$, $b$, $c$ each represent a length.

$$R = a^3 \qquad S = a + b + c \qquad T = (a + b)^2$$
$$U = 3a + 3b + 3c \qquad V = abc$$
$$W = ab^2 + ba^2 + cb^2$$

   (a) Which quantities could represent a volume?

..................................................................................................................................... (2)

   (b) For the others, say what they could represent.

..................................................................................................................................... (2)

3  Find the values of each of these expressions and state whether each one is rational or irrational:

$(a)\ \left(\sqrt{3} + 3\right) + \left(3 - \sqrt{3}\right)$ $\qquad (b)\ \left(\sqrt{3} + 3\right)\left(3 - \sqrt{3}\right)$

$(c)\ \dfrac{\sqrt{25}}{\sqrt{8}}$ $\qquad\qquad (d)\ \sqrt{3}\left(\sqrt{18} + \sqrt{27}\right)$

$(e)\ \sqrt{3} + \sqrt{18}$ $\qquad\qquad\qquad\qquad\qquad\qquad\qquad$ (5)

4  (a) Solve these simultaneous equations algebraically:

$$3x + 4y = -1$$
$$5x + 8y = 0$$

$\qquad\qquad\qquad\qquad\qquad\qquad\qquad\qquad\qquad\qquad\qquad\qquad$ (3)

   (b) Solve these inequalities:

   (i)  $7 - 4x \le 3$ $\qquad$ (ii)  $x^2 < 16$ $\qquad\qquad\qquad\qquad$ (2+2)

QUESTIONS **5** Sam and Ajit are playing a game with these cards:

They each take one card without looking.
(a) What is the probability that:

    (i) neither card is odd?........................................................................... (1)

    (ii) both cards are odd?........................................................................... (1)

    (iii) the number on Ajit's card is greater than the number on Sam's card?...........

 (2)

(b) Ajit takes his card first.

What is the probability that Sam takes the 3?............................................... (2)

**6** One solution of the quadratic equation

$$2x^2 + ax - 6 = 0$$
is $x = -2$

(a) Find the value of $a$.

 (2)

(b) Complete the solution of the equation.

................................................................................................................ (2)

**7** Here is a pattern made with match sticks:

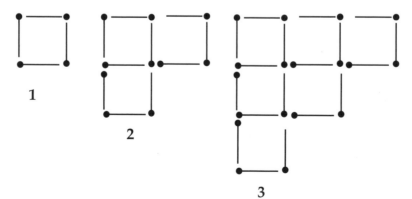

1

2

3

(a) Complete the table.

| Pattern number | 1 | 2 | 3 | 4 | 5 |
|---|---|---|---|---|---|
| Number of squares | 1 | 3 | 6 | 10 | |
| Number of matches | 4 | 10 | 18 | | |

(2)

(b) For
   (i)  the number of squares and
   (ii) the number of matches
   give the rule for finding the $(n+1)$th term from the $n$th term.

   .................................................................................................................. (2)

(c) Find
   (i)  the number of squares and
   (ii) the number of matches
   in pattern $n$.

   ..................................................................................................................

   .................................................................................................................. (4)

**8** (a) Make $b$ the subject of the formula

$$k = \frac{brt}{v - b}$$

(4)

(b) Write as simply as possible

   (i) $\dfrac{x^2 y}{\sqrt{y}}$   (ii) $\left(3x^2\right)^3$   (iii) $\dfrac{2xy^{-1}}{3x^{-1}y}$

(3)

(c) (i)  Write as a single fraction:

   $$\frac{2}{1+x} + \frac{1}{x}$$

(2)

   (ii) Solve the equation:

   $$\frac{4}{1+x} + \frac{2}{x} = 9$$

(4)

Section B *You may use a calculator.*

**9** The diagram shows a cylindrical metal block of length 30 cm and cross-sectional radius 5 cm.

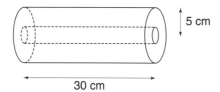

The block has a hole drilled through its centre which reduces the volume of the block by 20%.

(a) Calculate the radius of the hole.

......................................................................................................................................... (3)

(b) The cylinder rests on a block. This is its cross-section:

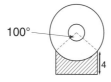

Find the area of cross-section (shaded in the diagram). [6]

**10** A sample of 180 '1 litre' bottles is taken from a production line and the capacities measured. This histogram represents the data:

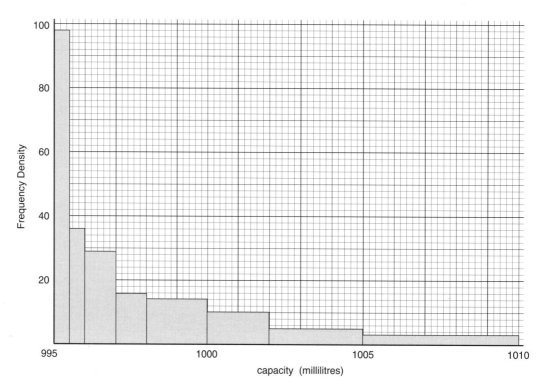

(a) What are the units on the Frequency Density axis?........................................................ (1)

Another production line sample gives these data:

| capacity, $c$, (ml) | Frequency |
|---|---|
| $995 \leqslant c < 996$ | 0 |
| $996 \leqslant c < 998$ | 3 |
| $998 \leqslant c < 999$ | 25 |
| $999 \leqslant c < 1000$ | 60 |
| $1000 \leqslant c < 1001$ | 76 |
| $1001 \leqslant c < 1002$ | 15 |
| $1002 \leqslant c < 1005$ | 1 |
| $1005 \leqslant c < 1010$ | 0 |

(b) Draw the histogram for the second sample on the same grid. (4)

(c) Use the histograms to compare the distribution.
    Make two comparisons. (2)

(d) Calculate estimates of the mean and standard deviation for the second sample. (5)

For the first sample, the mean = 998.2
and the standard deviation = 3.57

(e) Make two further comparisons between the two distributions. (2)

**11** This is part of the graph of $y = 3 \tan 5x$

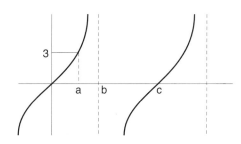

(a) Find the values of a, b and c. (3)

(b) Solve the equation $3 \tan 5x = -6$
    for $-30° \leqslant x \leqslant 30°$ (3)

**12**

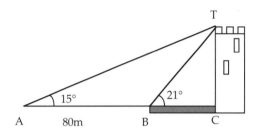

Mark wants to find the height of the tower TC.
BC is a river, so he measures:
  Angle of elevation at A = 15°
  Angle of elevation at B = 21°
  AB = 80m
(a) Find the height of the tower. (5)

All his measurements are subject to error
Angles ± 1°,  Length ± 0·5m
(b) Find the lowest height the tower could be. (4)

**13** Mr Jones drives to work. He passes three sets of traffic lights.
The probability he has to stop at the first set is 0·4. If he stops at a traffic light, the probability he has to stop at the next is 0·7.
If he does not stop, the probability of having to stop at the next is 0·4.

Find the probabilities that:
(a) he does not have to stop. (1)

(b) he stops at just one set. (4)

**14** The Great Pyramid of Cheops was built as a square based pyramid.
The length of each side of the square was 230·1 m. The height of the pyramid was 146·6 m.

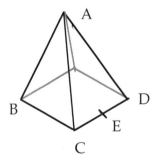

E is the mid point of CD.

(a) Find the angle AE makes with the base. (2)

(b) Find the angle BAC. (4)

# Answers

## 1 NUMBER

| Question | Answer | Mark |
|---|---|---|
| 1 (a) | $22\sin 70° = 20.67$, $\quad 28\sin 48° = 20.81$ | 2+1 |
| | Perpendicular distance between longest sides is nearly the same at each end. | 1 |
| | Longest sides are nearly parallel, so quadrilateral is roughly a trapezium. | 1 |

| | | |
|---|---|---|
| (b) | Area of largest possible trapezium must be found using upper bounds of lengths. | 1 |
| | Maximum area $= \frac{1}{2} \times 21.5 \times (32.5 + 58.5)$ | 1 |
| | $= 978.25$ | 1 |
| | Yes, this is less than 1000. | 1 |

**Examiner's tip** This could have been treated in a more complicated way by using the maximum possible distance between the 'parallel' sides, i.e. $28.5\sin 48.5°$, which is 21.3 and $22.5\sin 70.5°$, which is 21.2, both smaller than 21.5 which had been taken as the upper bound of 21. The result would clearly have been smaller.
In some problems it may be necessary to take a lower bound, even though the maximum value of the expression is required, for example where division is involved.

| | | |
|---|---|---|
| 2 (a) | $19.5 \times 29.5$ | 1 |
| | 575.25 | 1 |
| (b) | $(x + 0.5)^2 - (x - 0.5)^2$ | 1 |
| | $(x + 0.5 - x + 0.5)(x + 0.5 \; x - 0.5)$ or brackets expanded | 1 |
| | $2x$ | 1 |

**Examiner's tip** In part (b) you can expand both the brackets but it is neater and quicker to use the 'difference of two squares', $(x - y)(x + y) = x^2 - y^2$.

| | | |
|---|---|---|
| 3 (a) | For example, $\sqrt{20}$ or $\sqrt[3]{70}$ | 1 |
| (b) | As $N$ is rational, let $N = \dfrac{p}{q}$, where $p$ and $q$ are integers. | 1 |
| | Reciprocal of $N = \dfrac{q}{p}$, which is rational | 1 |

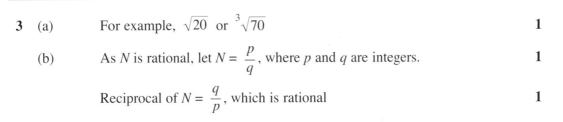

**Examiner's tip** In part (a), any irrational between the limits will be right. The proof in part (b) depends on the definition of a rational number, that is it can be expressed as an integer divided by an integer.

| Question | Answer | Mark |
|---|---|---|

**4**  Maximum average speed = $\dfrac{400.5}{49.35}$

$= 8.1155...$ or $8.11$

Marks: 2, 1

**Examiner's tip**  This is an example where the upper bound of the speed is obtained using the upper bound of the distance with the lower bound of the time. It is not sensible to round up since this would be above the upper bound.

---

**5**  (a)   $x^{-2}, \quad \dfrac{1}{x}, \quad x^{\frac{1}{2}}, \quad x$

Mark: 2

(b)   Opposite order.

Mark: 1

**Examiner's tip**  If in doubt, substitute numbers for $x$, e.g. 4 and $\dfrac{1}{4}$.

---

**6**  (a)   For example, $1.21$ or $1\dfrac{21}{100}$

Mark: 1

(b)   For example, $\sqrt{1.5}$ or $\sqrt{\dfrac{3}{2}}$

Mark: 1

**Examiner's tip**  You may have thought of different answers. They will be right so long as they fall between the limits and are rational/irrational. In part (b) it can help to square the limits (1.44, 1.5625) then choose a number between these. Its square root may be irrational – check. Of course, square roots are not the only irrational numbers.

---

**7**  (a)   Let $N = 15.\overset{\bullet}{4}0\overset{\bullet}{7}$

$1000N = 15407.\overset{\bullet}{4}0\overset{\bullet}{7}$

Mark: 1

Subtracting $999N = 15392$

$N = \dfrac{15392}{999}$ which is rational

Mark: 1

(b)   (i)   $2 + \sqrt{3} - (2 - \sqrt{3}) = 2\sqrt{3}$         irrational         1+1

(ii)   $(2 + \sqrt{3})(2 - \sqrt{3}) = 2^2 - (\sqrt{3})^2 = 4 - 3 = 1$         rational         1+1

(iii)   $(2 + \sqrt{3})^2 = 4 + 2 \times 2 \times \sqrt{3} + (\sqrt{3})^2 = 7 + 4\sqrt{3}$         irrational         1+1

**Examiner's tip**  Recurring decimals are always rational. To show this, multiply the number by a power of 10 so that the recurring pattern 'lines up'. Then subtract to remove the recurring part.

| Question | Answer | Mark |
|---|---|---|
| 8 (a) | $400 \times 27.95 = 11180 \, \text{mm}$ | 1+1 |
| | $= 11.18 \, \text{metres}$ | 1 |
| (b) | $\pi \left( \dfrac{28 \cdot 05}{2} \right)^2 \times 1 \cdot 95$ | 1+1 |
| | $= 1205 \, \text{mm}^3$ | 1 |

> **Examiner's tip** In each part, there will be a mark for identifying the correct value to use in the calculation.

| Question | Answer | Mark |
|---|---|---|
| 9 (a) | $3.142 = \dfrac{3142}{1000}$ which is rational | 1 |
| (b) | $1.\dot{6} = 1\frac{2}{3}$ which is rational | 1 |
| (c) | $\left( \sqrt{3} \right)^3 = 3\sqrt{3}$ which is irrational | 2 |
| (d) | $(1 + \sqrt{3})(1 - \sqrt{3}) = 1 + \sqrt{3} - \sqrt{3} - 3$ | 1 |
| | $= {}^-2$ which is rational | 1 |
| (e) | $\dfrac{\left( 1 + \sqrt{3} \right)}{\left( 1 - \sqrt{3} \right)} = \dfrac{\left( 1 + \sqrt{3} \right)\left( 1 + \sqrt{3} \right)}{\left( 1 - \sqrt{3} \right)\left( 1 + \sqrt{3} \right)} = \dfrac{1 + 2\sqrt{3} + 3}{{}^-2}$ | 2 |
| | $= -2 - \sqrt{3}$ which is irrational | 1 |

> **Examiner's tip** To show that a number is rational it is necessary to show that it can be written as a fraction using whole numbers. In this case an approach to part (e) was suggested by the work in part (d).

| Question | Answer | Mark |
|---|---|---|
| 10 (a) | 3.75 hours | 1 |
| | 195 miles,     205 miles | 1+1 |
| (b) | Upper bound $= \dfrac{205}{3.25}$ | 1 |
| | $= 63.1$ | 1 |
| | Lower bound $= \dfrac{195}{3.75}$ | 1 |
| | $= 52$ | 1 |

> **Examiner's tip** It is not asked here, but using measurements taken to this accuracy, it is not possible to state the speed as the bounds are different to one significant figure.

## 2 ALGEBRA

| Question | Answer | Mark |
|---|---|---|
| **1** (a) | Next term will be the mean of the previous two terms. | 1 |

(b) Next three terms are $1\frac{11}{16}$, $1\frac{21}{32}$, $1\frac{43}{64}$, or on the calculator 1.6875,

1.656 25, 1.671 85 — **1**

Two more terms: 1.664 0625, 1.667 956 25 — **1+1**

Limit appears to be $1\frac{2}{3}$. — **1**

---

**2** (a) $P = \dfrac{(40+15)(40-15+1)}{2} = 715$ — **1**

(b) $b = 2a$ — **1**

$P = \dfrac{(2a+a)(2a-a+1)}{2}$ — **1**

$= \dfrac{3a(a+1)}{2} = \dfrac{3a^2+3a}{2}$ — **1**

(c) $\dfrac{3a^2+3a}{2} = 975$

$3a^2 + 3a = 1950$

$a^2 + a - 650 = 0$ — **1**

$(a+26)(a-25) = 0$ — **1**

$a = 25, b = 50$ — **1**

Therefore possible.

---

**3** (a) The lengths of the three sides are $x$, $x$ and $22 - 2x$, since the total
length of netting is 22 m.

Area $= x(22 - 2x) = 60$ — **1**

$22x - 2x^2 = 60$    (expanding brackets)

$11x - x^2 = 30$    (dividing by 2) — **1**

$-x^2 + 11x - 30 = 0$    (subtracting 30 from each side)

$x^2 - 11x + 30 = 0$    (multiplying each side by $^-1$) — **1**

(b) $(x-5)(x-6) = 0$ — **1**

$x - 5 = 0$ or $x - 6 = 0$ — **1**

$x = 5$ or $6$ — **1**

| Question | Answer | Mark |
|---|---|---|

**Examiner's tip** Since the left-hand side of this equation did factorise, this is the easiest way to solve it. However, the same result would have been achieved by using the quadratic formula or completing the square.

(c)   If $x = 5$ the run measures 5 by 12                1
       If $x = 6$ the run measures 6 by 10                1

**Examiner's tip** Both solutions work in this practical problem. This is not always the case.

**4** (a)   $\sqrt{\dfrac{a^2 b^{-\frac{1}{2}}}{9}}$                1

$\dfrac{a}{3b^{\frac{1}{4}}}$ or $\dfrac{a}{3\sqrt[4]{b}}$ or $\dfrac{1}{3}ab^{-\frac{1}{4}}$                1

(b)   $t^2 = \dfrac{2s}{a}$                1

$t = \sqrt{\dfrac{2s}{a}}$                1

(c)   $\dfrac{(3x+1)(x-1)}{(x+1)(x-1)}$                1

$= \dfrac{(3x+1)}{(x+1)}$                1

**Examiner's tip** Cancel terms first in part (a).
Don't forget the factors of $x^2 - 1$ in part (c).

**5** (a)

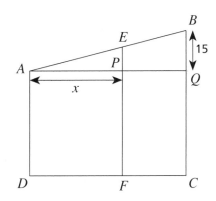

$APE$ and $AQB$ are similar triangles so

| Question | Answer | | Mark |
|---|---|---|---|
| | $\dfrac{PE}{QB} = \dfrac{AP}{AQ}$ | (ratios of corresponding sides) | 1 |
| | $PE = x \times 15 \div 60 = \frac{1}{4}x$ | (substituting) | |
| | $EF = FP + PE = 25 + \frac{1}{4}x$ | | 1 |
| (b) | Area of $AEFD = \frac{1}{2}x\,(AD + EF) = \frac{1}{2}x\,(25 + 25 + \frac{1}{4}x)$ | | 1 |
| | Area of $AEFD = \frac{1}{2}$ area $ABCD = \frac{1}{4} \times 60 \times (25 + 40)$ | | 1 |
| | $25x + \frac{1}{8}x^2 = 975$ | (simplifying and putting areas equal) | 1 |
| | $x^2 + 200x - 7800 = 0$ | (multiply by 8 and rearrange) | |

| Question | | | Mark |
|---|---|---|---|
| (c) | $x = 30$ | $x^2 + 200x - 7800 = -900$ | |
| | 35 | 425 | 1 |
| | 33 | $-111$ | |
| | 33.5 | 22.25 | |
| | 33.4 | $-4.44$ | 1 |
| | 33.4 is closer | | 1 |

**Examiner's tip**  As an alternative, if you know the method, you could use the quadratic formula or 'completing the square'. This quadratic expression did not factorise and there was a clue to this in the question – the answer was asked to the nearest 0.1 m.

| | | Mark |
|---|---|---|
| (d) | It is just to the right of halfway and $DF$ will be wider than $FC$ since $AD$ is shorter than $BC$. | 1 |

| Question | Answer | Mark |
|---|---|---|
| **6** (a) | Numerator $= (2x - 1)(x - 2)$ | 1 |
| | Denominator $= (x - 2)(x + 2)$ | 1 |
| | $\dfrac{2x-1}{x+2}$ | 1 |
| (b) | $x^2 - 2px + p^2 + q$ gives $p = 4$ | 1 |
| | $q = 1$ | 1 |

**Examiner's tip**  Notice that you could use the method in part (b) to solve an equation, except in this case, if you put $(x - 4)^2 + 1$ equal to 0, you would need to find the square root of negative one!

| Question | Answer | Mark |
|---|---|---|
| 7 | Let the lengths of the sides of the rectangle be $x$ and $y$. | |
| | $xy = 6$            (area of rectangle) | 1 |
| | $\sqrt{x^2 + y^2} = \sqrt{13}$ or $x^2 + y^2 = 13$   (using Pythagoras) | 1 |
| | $x^2 + \dfrac{36}{x^2} = 13$        (substituting for $y$ from first equation) | 1 |
| | $x^4 - 13x^2 + 36 = 0$     (multiplying each side by $x^2$ and rearranging) | 1 |
| | $(x^2 - 9)(x^2 - 4) = 0$      (factorising) | 1 |
| | $x^2 = 9$ or $4$, $x = 3$ or $2$ | 1 |
| | Rectangle is $3\,\text{m}$ by $2\,\text{m}$ or $2\,\text{m}$ by $3\,\text{m}$. | |

**Examiner's tip**   Although it looks as though this is an equation in $x^4$ it is only a quadratic in $x^2$, from the practical point of view. Notice that it is not necessary to consider the negative solutions since the problem was about actual lengths.

---

**8**  (a)

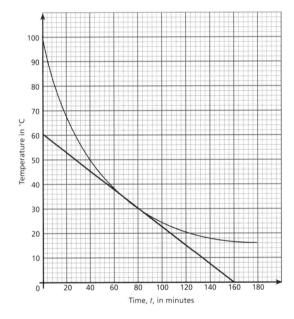

Time, $t$, in minutes

           1

(b)       $-\dfrac{60}{160} = -0.375$           2

          °C/minute          1

(c)       Rate of cooling         1

**Examiner's tip**   You will lose a mark in part (b) if you omit the negative sign.

---

**9**  (a)       If it were linear the increases would be in proportion:                                                  
               Speed goes up in steps of 20 but distance goes up by 100 then 140.      1

| Question | Answer | Mark |
|---|---|---|
| (b) | If $d \propto s^2$, then $\left(\dfrac{30}{50}\right)^2 (= 0.36)$ should equal $\left(\dfrac{75}{175}\right) (= 0.42...)$ | 1 |
| (c) | $75 = 30t + 900k$ | |
| | $175 = 50t + 2500k$ | 1 |
| | $375 = 150t + 4500k$     (multiplying first by 5) | |
| | $525 = 150t + 7500k$     (multiplying second by 3) | 1 |
| | $150 = 3000k$     (subtracting) | 1 |
| | $k = 0.05$ | 1 |
| | $t = (75 - 900 \times 0.05) \div 30 = 1$ | 1 |

> **Examiner's tip**   It is also possible to solve a problem like this by drawing the graph of $d$ against $s^2$ and finding the gradient and intercept.

| Question | Answer | Mark |
|---|---|---|
| **10** (a) | $x^{3/2}$ | 1 |
| (b) | $x^{-2}$ | 1 |
| (c) | $x^6 y^4$ | 1 |

> **Examiner's tip**   Notice in part (c) that the answer is not $x^5 y^4$ achieved by adding indices. It is perhaps clearer to see this if you treat $(x^3 y^2)^2$ as $(x^3 y^2) \times (x^3 y^2)$ where you can add the indices.

| Question | Answer | Mark |
|---|---|---|
| **11** (a) | $-1.38, -0.28, 2.68$ | 1 |
| (b) | Taking reading when $y = 1$ | 1 |
| | $-1.68, -0.56, 2.21$ | 1 |
| (c) | $x^3 - 4x - 1 = x - 2$ | 1 |
| | $y = x - 2$     drawn | 1 |
| | $-2.34, 0.20, 2.11$ | 2 |

> **Examiner's tip**   Draw x = 1 on the graph to show you have used it in (b). Some degree of error in the accuracy of the reading will be allowed so long as your results are correct to 1 d.p. Don't forget the scales are different on the two axes.

| Question | Answer | Mark |
|---|---|---|
| **12** (a) | Tangent drawn at $t = 4$ | 1 |
| | $42 \div 8 = 5.25$ | 1 |
| | Units m/s$^2$ | 1 |

> **Examiner's tip**   Try to draw the tangent so that it touches at time $t = 4$. Take the measurements to calculate the gradient as large as the diagram will allow.

| Question | Answer | Mark |
|---|---|---|
| (b) | Attempt at area under curve up to 10 seconds | **1** |
| | $\frac{1}{2}(0 + 55) + 12 + 23 + 31 + 37 + 42 + 46 + 50 + 52 + 54$ | |
| | (trapezium rule using 10 strips) | **2** |
| | $= 374.5$ or $370\,\text{m}$ | **1** |

 **Examiner's tip**  You could also have obtained this answer by using 5 strips or by counting squares.

---

| | | |
|---|---|---|
| **13** | $\frac{1}{2} \times 5 \times 0.95 + \frac{1}{2} \times 5 \times (0.95 + 0.9) + \frac{1}{2} \times 5 \times (0.9 + 0.55)$ | |
| | $+ \frac{1}{2} \times 5 \times (0.55 + 0.2) + \frac{1}{2} \times 5 \times 0.2$ | |
| | or $5 \times (0.95 + 0.9 + 0.55 + 0.2)$ | **2** |
| | $= 13\,\text{m}^2$ | **1** |

**Examiner's tip**  This trapezium method gives an underestimate, as the shape is largely convex. The triangles/trapezia leave out some area on most strips. Accuracy would be improved with more (narrower) strips. Alternatively, you could count squares. Care would be needed in deciding on the size of the square and what it represented. For example, if you chose squares measuring 2 mm by 2 mm, the total would be about 550. Each square represents $0.025\,\text{m}^2$, giving $13.75\,\text{m}^2$.

---

**14** (a)

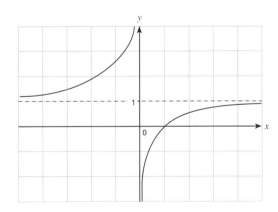

**2**

(b)

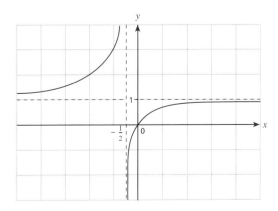

**2**

| Question | Answer | Mark |
|---|---|---|

**15**

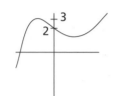 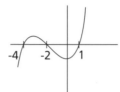 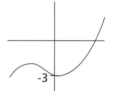 

**4**
(one mark each)

| | | |
|---|---|---|
| **16** (a) | $^-1.53, {^-}0.36, 1.90$ | **2** |
| (b) | Line $y = 1 - x$ drawn. | **1** |
| | $^-1, {^-}0.62, 1.62$ | **2** |

| | | |
|---|---|---|
| **17** | $x^2 + 6x + 9 < x^2 + 2x + 7$ | **1** |
| | $4x < -2$ | **1** |
| | $x < -\frac{1}{2}$ | **1** |

| | | |
|---|---|---|
| **18** | Denominator $(x + 2)(2x - 1)$ | **1** |
| | Numerators $2(2x - 1)$ and $3(x + 2)$ | **1** |
| | $4x - 2 + 3x + 6 = (x + 2)(2x - 1)$ | **1** |
| | $7x + 4 = 2x^2 + 3x - 2$ | **1** |
| | $2x^2 - 4x - 6 = 0$ or $x^2 - 2x - 3 = 0$ | **1** |
| | $(x - 3)(x + 1) = 0$ | **1** |
| | $x = 3$ or $x = -1$ | **1** |

| Question | Answer | Mark |
|---|---|---|

There is no need to write the combined fractions over the denominator as you can multiply both sides by $x + 2$ and $2x - 1$ at the start. You may also have combined some of the steps.

# 3 SHAPE, SPACE AND MEASURES

| Question | Answer | Mark |
|---|---|---|
| 1 | Scale factor for large ball from small ball = 3 | |
| | Volume scale factor = $3^3$ | 1 |
| | 27 small balls | 1 |

You can do this by working out the volumes using $\frac{4}{3}\pi r^3$ but this is unnecessary. It may help to think of how many 1 cm cubes will fit into a 3 cm cube:

| | | | |
|---|---|---|---|
| 2 | (a) | $\dfrac{36}{30} = \dfrac{36 - h}{10}$ | 1 |
| | | $12 = 36 - h \qquad h = 24$ | 1+1 |
| | (b) | Slant height of complete cone $= \sqrt{36^2 + 15^2}$ | 1 |
| | | $= 39$ | 1 |
| | | Slant height of small cone $= \frac{1}{3} \times 39 = 13$ | 1 |
| | | Surface area of complete cone $= \pi \times 15 \times 39$ | 1 |
| | | Surface area of small cone $= \pi \times 5 \times 13$ | 1 |
| | | Surface area of shade $= 585\pi - 65\pi = 520\pi = 1634\,\text{cm}^2$ | 1 |
| | | $\qquad$ (or 1630 cm$^2$ correct to 3 significant figures) | |

The first part is done using the ratios of corresponding sides in the similar triangles $VDB$ and $VCA$. You need the formula for the curved surface area of a cone for the second part, $\pi rl$, where $l$ is the slant height of the cone and $r$ is the radius of the base.

| | | | |
|---|---|---|---|
| 3 | (a) | $\pi \times 2.5^2 \times 20.5 = 402.5...$ | 1+1 |
| | | $\frac{4}{3} \times \pi \times 0.5^3 = 0.52...$ | 1+1 |
| | | $\pi \times 0.5^2 \times 19 = 14.92...$ | 1+1 |
| | | $= 418\,\text{cm}^3$ | 1 |
| | (b) | Multiply by $1.2^3$ | 1 |
| | | $= 722.3\,\text{cm}^3$ | 1 |

| Question | Answer | Mark |
|---|---|---|

**4** (a)      Triangle drawn 2 up and 2 to the left.      1

  (b)   (i)   $\mathbf{a} + \mathbf{b}$      1

      (ii)   $\mathbf{a} - \frac{1}{2}\mathbf{b}$      1

  (c)      $\overrightarrow{AD} = \overrightarrow{AB} + \overrightarrow{BD}$      1

           $= \mathbf{a} + \mathbf{b} + \frac{2}{3}(\mathbf{a} - \frac{1}{2}\mathbf{b})$      1

           $= \frac{5}{3}\mathbf{a} + \frac{2}{3}\mathbf{b}$      1+1

**5** (a)

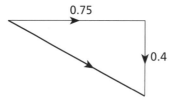

     (i)   $\sqrt{0.75^2 + 0.4^2}$      1

         $= 0.85$ m/s      1

     (ii)   $\arctan \frac{0.4}{0.75}$      1

         $= 28.1°$      1

  (b)   (i)   $\frac{15}{0.75} \times 0.4$      1

         $= 8$ m      1

      (ii)   $\frac{15}{0.75}$      1

         $= 20$ s      1

| Question | Answer | Mark |
|---|---|---|
| **6** (a) | $CD = 4$ | 1 |
| | $? = 4\tan 73°$ | 2 |
| | $= 13.08$ | 1 |
| (b) | $? = \sqrt{13^2 - 4^2}$ | 2 |
| | $= 12.37$ | 1 |
| (c) | Cosine rule: $130^2 = 169^2 + 169^2 - 2 \times 169 \times 169\cos x$ | 2 |
| | $x = 45.239...$ | 2 |
| | $? = 169\sin x$ | 1 |
| | $= 120$ | 1 |

**Examiner's tip**  In parts (a) and (b), the symmetry of the isosceles triangles must be used to find the side of the right-angled triangle. Part (c) is not a symmetrical situation although you could use symmetry to start to solve the problem:

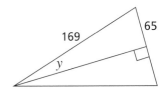

$y = \arc\sin(65/169) = 22.619...$
$x = 2y = 45.239...$

| Question | Answer | Mark |
|---|---|---|
| **7** (a) | 1 to 50 | 1 |
| (b) | 2.0 | 1 |
| (c) | $2.5^2 + 2^2$ | 1 |
| | $= 10.25$ | 1 |
| | $\sqrt{10.25} = 3.20...$ The pole is too long | 1 |
| (d) | Width of shed $= 1.75\,\text{m}$ | |
| | Two longer positions: | |

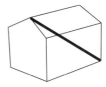

$\sqrt{2^2 + 2.5^2 + 0.875^2}$  — 2
$= 3.3189...$  — 1

Height at side $= 1.5\,\text{m}$
$\sqrt{1.5^2 + 1.75^2 + 2.5^2} = 3.400...$  — 1
This is the longest.  — 1

| Question | Answer | Mark |
|---|---|---|

| 8 | Square joining centres has side 2 cm | 1 |
| | Diagonal of square $= \sqrt{2^2 + 2^2}$ | 1 |
| | $= 2.828\ldots$ | 1 |
| | Radius of container = small radius + half diagonal of square | 1 |
| | $= 2.414 = 2.41$ | 1 |

| 9 (a) | First high tide when $\sin(29.2t)° = 1$, i.e. when $29.2t = 90$ | 1 |
| | $t = 3.082\ldots$ hours: Time is 3.05 am (to nearest minute) | 1 |

| (b) | First low tide when $\sin(29.2t)° = -1$, i.e. when $29.2t = 270$ | 1 |
| | $t = 9.246\ldots$ hours: Time is 9.15 am (to nearest minute) | 1 |
| (c) | $t = 24$, depth $= L + K\sin(700.8)° = L + (-0.3288\ldots)K$ | 1 |
| | The water level is lower on 2 July. | 1 |

| (d) | $t = 96$, depth $= L + K\sin(2803.2)° = L + (-0.9735\ldots)K$ | 1 |
| | $t = 96.1$, depth $= L + K\sin(2806.12)° = L + (-0.9606\ldots)K$ | 1 |
| | This is higher so the tide is rising. | 1 |

| Question | Answer | Mark |
|---|---|---|
| **10** | 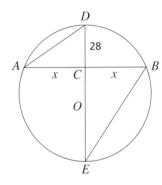 $AC^2 = 170^2 - 142^2$ | 1 |
| | $\quad\quad\;\; = 8736$ | 1 |
| | $AC = 93.46...$ | 1 |
| | $AB = 2 \times AC = 186.9$ m | 1 |

Alternative method:

Using complete circle and diameter $DE$,
triangles $ADC$ and $EBC$ are similar      **1**

$CE = 2 \times 170 - 28 = 312$      **1**

$AC = CB = x$

$$\frac{x}{28} = \frac{312}{x}$$      **1**

$2x = 2 \times \sqrt{8736} = 186.9$ m      **1**

> **Examiner's tip** This shows two ways of tackling this problem. The first (and simplest on this occasion) uses Pythagoras and the other depends on similar triangles. The triangles are similar since angle $DAB$ = angle $DEB$, subtending the same arc $DB$. Similarly angle $ADE$ = angle $ABE$.

| | | |
|---|---|---|
| **11** (a) | EB = EF = 4, ED (hypotenuse) common | 1 |
| | Angle EBC = 90° Angle EFD = 90° (radius and tangent) | 1 |
| | Triangles congruent (RHS) | 1 |
| (b) | $BD = 4\tan 60°$    (or $\dfrac{4}{\tan 30°}$ ) | 1 |
| | $= 6{\cdot}93$m | 1 |
| (c) | $HD = \dfrac{BD}{\cos 60°}$ | 1 |
| | $= 13{\cdot}86$m | 1 |

> **Examiner's tip** In part (a) make sure you give your reasons. This case of congruence is 'right angle, hypotenuse and another side'.

| Question | Answer | Mark |
|---|---|---|

**12 (a)**    (i)   $BQ = \sqrt{1.05^2 + 2.33^2}$      1

$= 2.56$      1

(ii)   Angle $BQP = \arctan \dfrac{1.05}{2.33}$      2

$= 24.26°$      1

(iii)   Arc $QS = \dfrac{2 \times 24.26...}{360}$ of full circle radius 2.56 m      1

$= \dfrac{2 \times 24.26...}{360} \times 2 \times \pi \times 2.56...$      1

$= 2.16\,\text{m}$      1

**(b)**    Area of end is sector $SBQ$ + triangle $SRB$ + triangle $QBP$      1

$= \dfrac{2 \times 24.26...}{360} \times \pi \times 2.56...^2 + 1.05 \times 2.33$      2

$= 5.21$      1

> **Examiner's tip**   The multiplier for the sector as a fraction of the whole circle is the same for area as arc length. The two triangles in part (b) are the same size and together make a rectangle. Answers may differ from these if you use earlier rounded answers.

**(c)**    (i)   $2.1 \times \dfrac{1}{19} = 0.1105\,\text{m}$ or $11.05\,\text{cm}$      1

(ii)   $5.21 \times \left(\dfrac{1}{19}\right)^2$      1

$= 0.0144\,\text{m}^2$ or $144\,\text{cm}^2$      1

> **Examiner's tip**   Remember the area scale factor is squared and there are $10\,000\,\text{cm}^2$ in $1\,\text{m}^2$.

**13 (a)**      100°      1

**(b)**      130°      1

**(c)**      82°      1

**(d)**      Angle $OAC = 40°$      1

         Angle $OAB = 42°$      1

> **Examiner's tip**   Many questions set on this topic will require you to give a reason for each part. These are suitable forms of the reasons here: angle at centre; opposite angle of cyclic quadrilateral; angle in the alternate segment; isosceles triangle.

| Question | Answer | Mark |
|---|---|---|
| 14 | $\pi \times 58^2 - \pi \times 16^2$ | 1+1 |
| | $\times \dfrac{110}{360}$ | 1 |
| | = 2980 (to 3 significant figures) | 1 |

**Examiner's tip** The question did not specify the accuracy for the answer nor did it ask for appropriate accuracy. However, to give more than three significant figures is inappropriate from data to only two figures.

| | | |
|---|---|---|
| 15 (a) | $AC^2 = 8^2 + 6^2$ | 1 |
| | $AC = \sqrt{100} = 10$ | 1 |
| (b) | $AC^2 = AV^2 + VC^2 - 2\,AV \times VC \times \cos AVC$ | 1 |
| | $\cos AVC = \dfrac{8^2 + 5^2 - 100}{2 \times 5 \times 8} = -0.1375$ | 1 |
| | Angle $AVC = 97.9°$ | 1 |
| (c) | Using the sine rule, $\sin VAC = \dfrac{5}{10}\sin AVC\ (=0.4952...)$ | 1 |
| | $VN = 8\sin VAC = 3.96$ | 1+1 |

**Examiner's tip** Most calculators will give the obtuse angle for the negative cosine in part (b). The height in part (c) could have been found using the area of triangle AVC instead of the sine rule:

$$\frac{1}{2} \times 8 \times 5 \times \sin AVC = \frac{1}{2} \times VN \times 10$$

| | | |
|---|---|---|
| 16 (a) | Angle $APB = 80°$ | 1 |
| | $AB^2 = 4.5^2 + 9.2^2 - 2 \times 4.5 \times 9.2 \times \cos 80°$ | 1 |
| | $AB = 9.51\,\text{km}$ | 1 |
| (b) | $\dfrac{\sin PBA}{9.2} = \dfrac{\sin 80}{AB}$ | 1 |
| | Angle $PBA = 72.2°$ | 1 |
| | Bearing $= 72.2 - 63 = 009.2 = 009°$ | 1 |

**Examiner's tip** When you have sorted out the angles, this is a straight-forward application of the cosine and sine rules. Mark angles and distances on the diagram at the start and don't be tempted to measure!

# 4 HANDLING DATA

| Question | Answer | Mark |
|---|---|---|
| **1** (a) | (2), 5, 10, 15, 10, 8 | **3** |
| (b)(i) | Many people will not shop in the morning or on Thursday. | **1** |
| (ii) | Ask people over several days at differing times. | **1** |

> **Examiner's tip**  An area of 2 square centimetres on the histogram represents a frequency of 5 people.

**2** (a)     BRAND A                                        BRAND B

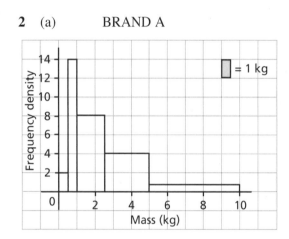 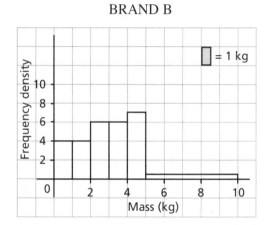

(1 mark deducted for each mistake) **3+3**

> **Examiner's tip**  The sizes of the classes vary in these distributions so the heights of the columns must be adjusted to make the area of the columns equal the frequency in each class. The axis up the page is Frequency density. You must decide on a unit area.

(b)     Brand A mid-points: 0.25, 0.75, 1.75, 3.75, 7.5
        Brand B mid-points: 0.5, 1.5, 2.5, 3.5, 4.5, 7.5          **1**

| A | Mean: 2.62 | SD: 1.93 |
|---|---|---|
| B | Mean: 3.27 | SD: 1.93 |

**1+1**

**1+1**

(c)     Higher mean (better yield on average) from Brand B          **1**
        Same spread (same degree of variation from the mean)        **1**

> **Examiner's tip**  A calculator with statistics makes these calculations much simpler and you would probably only have to do one in an examination.

**3** (a)     $\dfrac{3}{12} \times \dfrac{2}{11}$          **1+1**

| Question | Answer | Mark |
|---|---|---|
| | $=\dfrac{1}{22}$ | 1 |
| (b) | $\dfrac{4}{12}\times\dfrac{8}{11}$ | 1 |
| | $+\dfrac{5}{12}\times\dfrac{7}{11}$ | 1 |
| | $+\dfrac{3}{12}\times\dfrac{9}{11}$ | 1 |
| | $=\dfrac{47}{66}$ | 1 |

**Examiner's tip** In part (b) it is necessary to break the problem down into all the possibilities. The first probability is for red then not red, the second for green then not green and the third for yellow then not yellow. As they are all alternatives, add them up.

| | | | |
|---|---|---|---|
| **4** | (a) | No – more boys than girls. | 1 |
| | (b) | Sample 80 from 798 | 1 |
| | | Approximately 1 in 10 | 1 |
| | | Year 8: 15 pupils | 1 |
| | | (or $80\times\dfrac{150}{798}=15$) | |

**Examiner's tip** This question is about choosing a stratified sample to represent the population for the survey. You were not asked for the number of boys and girls separately but 15 divided in the ratio 85:65 is 9:6 to the nearest whole number.

| | | | |
|---|---|---|---|
| **5** | (a) | Roast beef 0.6, fruit 0.2 | 1 |
| | (b) | $0.6\times0.8=0.48$ | 1+1 |
| | (c) | Probabilities right for main course | 1 |
| | | sweet course | 1+1 |

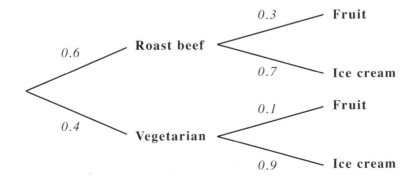

| Question | Answer | Mark |
|---|---|---|
| (d) | $0.6 \times 0.7 + 0.4 \times 0.9$ | **1+1** |
| | $= 0.42 + 0.36 = 0.78$ | **1** |

**Examiner's tip** In part (c) there is one mark for each pair of probabilities right on the tree diagram.

**6** Frequency Density scale should be marked 1 every 2cm. | **1**

Column heights    120 – 140    4 (given)
                          140 – 150    6
                          150 – 160    7
                          160 – 165    8
                          165 – 180    4                               **3**

**Examiner's tip** The frequency density is measured in number of pupils per centimetre of height. You will lose 1 mark for each error.

| Question | Answer | | Mark |
|---|---|---|---|
| **7** (a) | Probability (Double Fault) | $= 0.4 \times 0.05$ | **1+1** |
| | | $= 0.02$ | **1** |
| (b) | Probability (Win) | $= 0.6 \times 0.75$ | **1** |
| | | $+\ 0.4 \times 0.95 \times 0.5$ | **1+1** |
| | | $= 0.64$ | **1** |

**Examiner's tip** In part (b) Gabriella can win either with the first serve (0.6×0.75) or with the second serve if the first is not successful (0.4×0.95×0.5), the use of 0.4 earning the first mark.

**8** (a)    (i)

     (ii)    $\dfrac{5}{6} \times \dfrac{1}{6} = \dfrac{5}{36}$                        **1+1**

     (iii) Probability he wins $= 1 -$ (probability he does not win)        **1**

$$= 1 - \left(\frac{5}{6}\right)^3 = \frac{91}{216} \text{ or } 0.421$$        **1+1**

| Question | Answer | Mark |
|----------|--------|------|

Notice that the last part can be calculated from the probability he wins first throw, or the probability he wins second throw, or the probability he wins third throw, i.e.,

$$\frac{1}{6} + \frac{5}{6} \times \frac{1}{6} + \frac{5}{6} \times \frac{5}{6} \times \frac{1}{6}$$

(b)  (i)

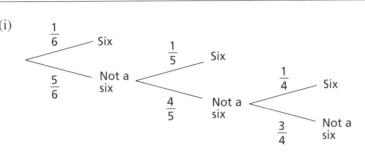

2

(ii)  $\dfrac{5}{6} \times \dfrac{1}{5} = \dfrac{1}{6}$   1+1

(iii)  $1 - \dfrac{5}{6} \times \dfrac{4}{5} \times \dfrac{3}{4}$   1

$= 1 - \dfrac{3}{6} = \dfrac{1}{2}$   1+1

**Examiner's tip** The argument is the same as in part (a) except that conditional probabilities are used because the cards are not replaced. Note that you may have answered parts (iii) and (iv) the other way round.

(iv)  As 3 cards are drawn, the probability that they contain the six is $\dfrac{3}{6} = \dfrac{1}{2}$.  1

| Question | Answer | Mark |
|---|---|---|
| **9** | Frequency Density scale marked or unit of area shown | **1** |
| | Column heights (see below) | **3** |

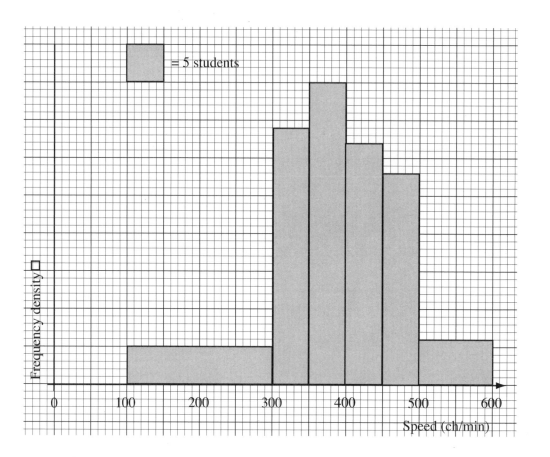

---

**Examiner's tip** If you choose a frequency density of one student per 5 characters/minute, the scale should be marked 1 for every 2 cm. In this case it is easier to use the alternative definition, choosing an area of $1\,cm^2$ to represent 5 students.

---

| | | | | Mark |
|---|---|---|---|---|
| **10** | (a) | (i) | $1.6 \times 10 = 16$ | **1** |
| | | (ii) | $1.4 \times 20 + 0.4 \times 40 = 44$ | **1+1** |
| | (b) | | Frequency densities: 1.1, 3.8, 2.7, 0.7, 0.2 | **3** |
| | | | columns drawn    heights correct | **1** |
| | | | widths correct | **1** |
| | | | *(see diagram on next page)* | |

| Question | Answer | Mark |
|---|---|---|

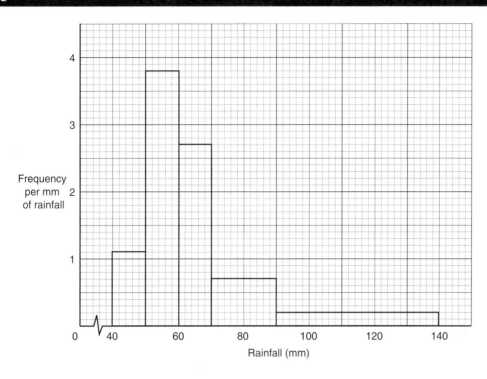

(c)  Range of amounts of rain the same.
Average rainfall higher in north (mode 70–80, 50–60)
Very few had high rainfall in the south, few had low rainfall in the north.  **3**

**Examiner's tip**  The comparison in part (c) should refer to the rainfall not the shape of the graph. There is one mark for each.

**11** (a)  1, 1.8, 2.1, 1.1, 0.8  **1**

(b)

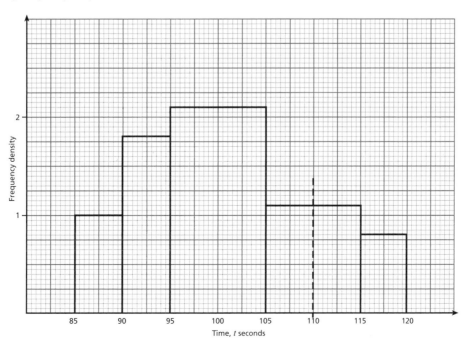

Scales marked  **1**

| Question | Answer | Mark |
|---|---|---|
| | Column widths correct | 1 |
| | Column heights correct | 1 |
| (c) | $\sqrt{\frac{1}{10}\left(93^2 + 90^2 + \ldots + 92^2\right) - 89.5^2}$ | 1 |
| | $= 3.1$ | 1 |
| (d) | Area of histogram to right of $110 = 4 + 5.5$ | 1 |
| | Proportion $= \frac{9.5}{50} = 0.19$ | 1 |

> **Examiner's tip** The frequency density has been found by dividing the frequency by the width of the class in each case. The result in part (d) is an estimate because we do not know how the times were distributed in the interval – they could all have been 105 seconds!

| | | |
|---|---|---|
| **12** (a) | $\frac{1}{8}$ | 1 |
| (b) | $\frac{3}{8} \times \frac{1}{5} = \frac{3}{40}$ | 1+1 |
| (c)(i) | $\frac{1}{8} \times \frac{1}{5} = \frac{1}{40}$ | 1 |
| (ii) | Probability (G secretary, B treasurer) $= \frac{1}{8} \times \frac{1}{3}$ | 1 |
| | Probability (G and B) $= \frac{1}{8} \times \frac{1}{5} + \frac{1}{8} \times \frac{1}{3} = \frac{1}{15}$ | 1+1 |

> **Examiner's tip** Make sure your fractions are right!

| | | | |
|---|---|---|---|
| **13** (a) | (i) | $(28 + \ldots + 27) \div 10$ | 1 |
| | | $= 32$ marks | 1 |
| | (ii) | $\sqrt{\frac{1}{10}\left(28^2 + \ldots + 27^2\right) - 32^2}$ | 1 |
| | | $= 11.9$ marks | 1 |
| (b) | | Boys' mean higher. | 1 |
| | | Boys' scores more variable. | 1 |

> **Examiner's tip** The formula used here for the standard deviation is
>
> 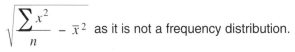 $\sqrt{\dfrac{\sum x^2}{n} - \bar{x}^2}$ as it is not a frequency distribution.
>
> Suitable formulae will be found at the front of the question paper. You may also use the statistics functions on your calculator.

| Question | Answer | Mark |
|----------|--------|------|
| **14** | Probability of at least one head $= 1 -$ (probability of no head) | **1** |
| | Probability of no head in $n$ tosses $= (0.5)^n$ | **1** |
| | $1 - (0.5)^n > 0.95$ | **1** |
| | $(0.5)^n < 0.05$ | **1** |
| | $(0.5)^4 < 0.0625, \ (0.5)^5 < 0.03125$, so $n = 5$ | **1** |
| **15** (a) | $0.35 + 0.57 - 0.15$ | **2** |
| | $= 0.77$ | **1** |
| (b) | $1 - 0.77$ | **1** |
| | $= 0.23$ | **1** |
| (c) | $0.35 - 0.15$ | **1** |
| | $= 0.20$ | **1** |

 **Examiner's tip**   You may find it useful to use a diagram, e.g.

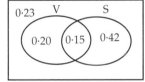

# 5 MOCK EXAMINATION PAPER

| Question | Answer | Mark |
|---|---|---|
| **1** (a) | $1 \times 10^9 \times 1 \times 10^{11} = 1 \times 10^{20}$ | 1+1 |
| (b) | $4 \times 10^{11} \div (5 \times 10^9) = 80$ | 1+1 |

**Examiner's tip** You should be able to do this without your calculator.

| | | |
|---|---|---|
| **2** (a) | R, V, W | 2 |
| (b) | S = length, T = area, U = length | 2 |

**Examiner's tip** You will lose a mark for any mistake.

| | | |
|---|---|---|
| **3** (a) | 6 (rational) | 1 |
| (b) | 6 (rational) | 1 |
| (c) | $\dfrac{5}{2\sqrt{2}}$  (irrational) | 1 |
| (d) | $3\sqrt{6} + 9$ (irrational) | 1 |
| (e) | $\sqrt{3} + 3\sqrt{2}$  (irrational) | 1 |

**Examiner's tip** You could leave the answer to part (d) as $3\sqrt{2}\sqrt{3} + 9$ or even $\sqrt{54} + 9$.

| | | | |
|---|---|---|---|
| **4** (a) | | $6x + 8y = -2$ | 1 |
| | | $5x + 8y = 0$ | |
| | | $x \quad\;\; = -2$ | 1 |
| | | $y \quad\; = 1.25$ | 1 |
| (b) | (i) | $-4x \le -4$ | 1 |
| | | $x \ge 1$ | 1 |
| | (ii) | $-4 < x < 4$ | 1+1 |

**Examiner's tip** Take care with the ≤ sign in part (b)(i). If in doubt about what happens when you divide by −4, add $4 + 4x$ to each side giving $4 \le 4x$, then divide by 4.

| | | | |
|---|---|---|---|
| **5** (a) | (i) | $\dfrac{2}{5} \times \dfrac{1}{4} = \dfrac{1}{10}$ | 1 |

| Question | Answer | Mark |
|---|---|---|
| (ii) | $\dfrac{3}{5} \times \dfrac{2}{4} = \dfrac{3}{10}$ | 1 |
| (iii) | No card same, outcome symmetrical | 1 |
| | $\dfrac{1}{2}$ | 1 |
| (b) | $\dfrac{4}{5} \times \dfrac{1}{4} = \dfrac{1}{5}$ | 1+1 |

> **Examiner's tip** In part (a)(iii) the reasons were not required and the answer 1/2 would score both marks.

---

| | | | Mark |
|---|---|---|---|
| 6 | (a) | $8 - 2a - 6 = 0$ | 1 |
| | | $a = 1$ | 1 |
| | (b) | $2x^2 + x - 6 = (2x - 3)(x + 2)$ | 1 |
| | | other solution $\quad x = 1\dfrac{1}{2}$ | 1 |

---

| | | | | Mark |
|---|---|---|---|---|
| 7 | (a) | | 15 | |
| | | | 28  40 | 2 |
| | (b) | (i) | Add $n + 1$ | 1 |
| | | (ii) | Add $6 + 2(n - 1)$ or $2n + 4$ | 1 |
| | (c) | (i) | $\dfrac{1}{2}n(n + 1)$ or $\dfrac{1}{2}n^2 + \dfrac{1}{2}n$ | 2 |
| | | (ii) | $n(n + 1) + 2n$ or $n^2 + 3n$ | 2 |

> **Examiner's tip** Part of the correct result in parts (c)(i) and (ii) will score 1 mark. It may help to see the result in (c)(ii) if you break up the pattern:

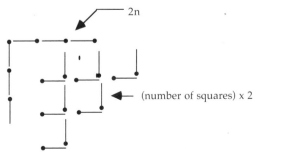

| Question | Answer | Mark |
|---|---|---|
| 8 (a) | $k(v - b) = brt$ | 1 |
| | $kv - kb = brt$ | 1 |
| | $b(rt + k) = kv$ | 1 |
| | $b = \dfrac{kv}{rt + k}$ | 1 |
| (b) (i) | $x^2\sqrt{y}$ | 1 |
| (ii) | $27x^6$ | 1 |
| (iii) | $\dfrac{2x^2}{3y^2}$ | 1 |
| (c) (i) | $\dfrac{2x + (1 + x)}{x(1 + x)} = \dfrac{3x + 1}{x(1 + x)}$ | 1+1 |
| (ii) | $6x + 2 = 9x(x + 1)$ | 1 |
| | $9x^2 + 3x - 2 = 0$ | 1 |
| | $x = \dfrac{1}{3} \text{ or } -\dfrac{2}{3}$ | 1+1 |

> **Examiner's tip** As this question is in the non-calculator section of the paper, you would not be expected to use the formula, so look for factors.

| Question | Answer | Mark |
|---|---|---|
| 9 (a) | Area of centre $= 0.2 \times \pi \times 5^2$ | 1 |
| | $r = \sqrt{\dfrac{0 \cdot 2 \times \pi \times 5^2}{\pi}}$ | 1 |
| | $= \sqrt{5} = 2.24$ | 1 |
| (b) | | |
| | $x = 2 \times 5 \sin 50°$ | 1 |
| | Area of rectangle $= 40 \sin 50°$ | 1 |
| | Area of triangle $= \dfrac{1}{2} \times 25 \times \sin 100°$ | 1 |
| | Area of sector $= \dfrac{100}{360} \times 25\pi$ | 1 |

| Question | Answer | Mark |
|---|---|---|

Shaded area $= 40 \sin 50° + 12 \cdot 5 \sin 100° - \dfrac{250\pi}{36}$     **1**

$= 21 \cdot 1$     **1**

> **Examiner's tip** Don't work out any numerical answers until the end. The value of $\pi$ divided out in part (a) and you could introduce rounding errors in (b).

**10** (a)     Number per millilitre     **1**

(b)     **4**

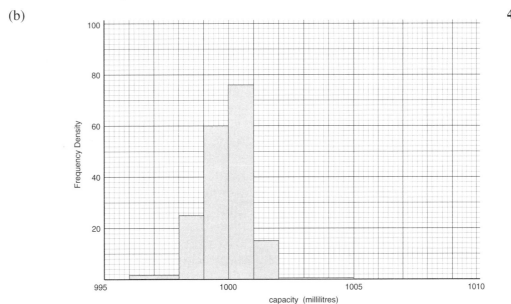

(c)     First skewed, second symmetrical     1 mark each for 2
First has lower average than second     out of the three
First has larger range than second     **2**

(d)     Mean $= 999.9$
Standard deviation $= 0.95$     **5**

(e)     Second has much higher mean     **1**

Second has far less spread,
(much smaller standard deviation)     **1**

> **Examiner's tip** You may score partial marks for the histogram if you make mistakes and for the mean and standard deviation if you have shown working. However, if you do it on your calculator, make sure you do it twice as a check.

| Question | Answer | Mark |
|----------|--------|------|
| 11 (a) | 9, 18, 36 | 1+1+1 |
| (b) | $\tan 5x = -2$ | 1 |
| | $5x = -63.4, 116.6$ | 1 |
| | $x = -12.7, 23.3$ | 1 |

| Question | Answer | Mark |
|----------|--------|------|
| 12 (a) | Angle ATB = 6° | 1 |
| | $BT = \dfrac{80 \times \sin 15°}{\sin 6°}$ | 1 |
| | $TC = BT \sin 21° = \dfrac{80 \times \sin 15° \times \sin 21°}{\sin 6°}$ | 1+1 |
| | = 70.99 or 71 m | 1 |
| (b) | Height = $\dfrac{80 \times \sin 15° \times \sin 21°}{\sin 6°}$ | |
| | Use 79.5, 14°, 20° | 1 |
| | Lowest height = 62.9 | 1 |
| | Use 79.5, 14°, 22° (hence Angle ATB = 8°) | 1 |
| | Lowest height = 51.8 | 1 |

| Question | Answer | Mark |
|----------|--------|------|
| 13 (a) | $(0.6)^3 = 0.216$ | 1 |
| (b) | stops at only first lights    $0.4 \times 0.3 \times 0.6$ | 1 |
| | stops at only second lights   $0.6 \times 0.4 \times 0.3$ | 1 |
| | stops at only third lights    $0.6 \times 0.6 \times 0.4$ | 1 |
| | Total =              0.288 | 1 |
| 14 (a) | Tan (angle with base) = $\dfrac{146 \cdot 6}{115 \cdot 05}$ | 1 |
| | Angle AE makes with base = 51.9° | 1 |
| (b) | BD = $230.1 \times \sqrt{2}$ = 325.4 m | 1 |
| | BA = $\sqrt{146.6^2 + 162.7^2}$ = 219 m | 1 |
| | $\sin(\tfrac{1}{2} \text{ angle BAC}) = \dfrac{115.05}{219}$ = 31.7° | 1 |
| | Angle BAC = 63.4° | 1 |